# Christmas
# TREASURES

# *Christmas* TREASURES

*A Collection of Heartwarming True Christmas Stories*

JENNIE HANSEN, HANK SMITH, GALE SEARS,
JENNIFER MOORE, SHAUNA HUMPHREYS, BRENT L. TOP,
RICHARD J. ALLEN, JENNY PROCTOR, MIKE WINDER,
M. R. DURBIN, KRISTEN MCKENDRY, JEANETTE MILLER

Covenant Communications, Inc.

Cover image: *Hand-drawn Christmas Ornaments* © mishkom, courtesy istockphoto.com

Cover design copyright © 2014 by Covenant Communications, Inc.

Published by Covenant Communications, Inc.
American Fork, Utah

Printed in the United States of America
First Printing: October 2014

20 19 18 17 16 15 14    10 9 8 7 6 5 4 3 2 1

ISBN 978-1-62108-879-0

# Contents

# Santa Loves Me

BY JENNIE HANSEN

It's hard to explain why that Christmas stuck in my mind. Perhaps it's because it's really two stories, mine and my father's. I was only five, but I remember there was so much snow that the path from our basement house to the barn was more tunnel than trail. My brothers dug a cave tall enough that I could stand up in it. My older brothers and sister were home each day, and I wasn't sure if it was because of Christmas or because the school bus couldn't get through the unplowed roads. My older sister and I spent a lot of time playing school and dreaming of the wonders displayed in the Montgomery Ward catalog. Christmas was coming, and I was confident Santa Claus would leave magical wonders under our tree for me. I loved Santa and was firmly convinced he loved me.

Like any five-year-old, I grew increasingly excited as Christmas drew near, but for some strange reason, Mama was tight-lipped and quiet. She frequently stood on a chair and stared out our basement-house window, looking toward the road that passed by our farm at the end of a long lane.

One morning I awoke to a strange kind of darkness. The lights dangling from a wire in each room were burning, but they didn't do much to brighten the rooms. There was something almost eerie about the strange half light and the silence.

Wandering from the bedroom, I noticed my teenage brothers pulling on their winter coats and boots. I discovered that only two of them were headed to the barn to help Daddy with chores. The oldest, Jerry, was assigned to shovel the new snow that had fallen during the night off the roof and away from the windows. So much snow had fallen during the night that our house was buried! At the time, that seemed exciting. I wanted to help, but Mama said no, and reluctantly, I dressed and ate my breakfast in front of the big coal range in the kitchen.

Giggling, my sisters and I listened to the scraping on the roof and tried to convince our younger brother and sister that Santa Claus was up there making a trial landing. After awhile, we could tell someone else was helping Jerry clear the roof, and then Daddy came into the house with a bucket of milk. He informed Mama that he and Ronnie would be taking hay to the cattle and sheep that were some distance from the barn and Ralph would stay to help Jerry clear snow from the roof.

"I want to go!" I made a dash for my boots. I loved riding on the big hay wagon. Daddy had removed the wheels and put runners on the wagon, turning it into a giant sled he and my brothers would load each morning with hay for the stock. There was something thrilling about riding on the big sled one or both of our teams of workhorses pulled.

"Not this time. Finish your breakfast." He pulled his hat low over his ears and dashed back up the stairs.

I was the one who wanted to go with Daddy, but it was Mama who wiped away a tear with the corner of her apron. I didn't know why she was sad; it was only a few days until Christmas, and it seemed everyone should be happy.

"I think she feels bad because we don't have any Christmas cards," my sister MarJean whispered. She was seven and knew lots of things.

I looked around. MarJean was right; no Christmas cards were pinned to the yarn "clothesline" stretched across one end of the living room. I knew that for some holidays and on our birthdays, cards came in the mail from our grandparents and from a lady Mama worked for a long time ago, before she'd married Daddy. I hadn't given mail delivery much thought, but it must have been more than a week since the mailman had left anything in our mailbox at the end of the lane. It only made sense that if the school bus couldn't make it through the drifts that covered the road, the mailman couldn't either. Getting cards and letters in the mail was always fun, but I wasn't sure why the absence of those cards was making Mama so sad. Nothing could dampen my enthusiasm for Christmas and Santa's visit.

A loud crash followed by the tinkle of falling glass interrupted my thoughts, and we all raced into the living room to discover glass and snow all over the couch and floor. Jerry was yelling, and Mama burst into tears. Poor Jerry! He'd shoveled a bit too vigorously and sent his shovel right through the living room window.

"Take the little kids into the bedroom until I get this cleaned up," Mama ordered MarJean and me. Reluctantly, we dragged our younger siblings from the room. When we were finally permitted to return, there was no sign of the snow or glass, and the room was darker than before, with a board nailed to the place where the window had been.

Two days passed, and Christmas Eve was only one day away. Mama spent a lot of time in the kitchen making candy and cookies. She also disappeared frequently to her bedroom, and we could hear the steady clack of her treadle sewing machine from behind the closed door.

Being helpful as only teenage boys could be, our brothers warned us younger kids that Santa wasn't going to come this year. There was too much snow, and even his reindeer couldn't get through the drifts. I didn't believe them. After all, reindeer could fly; they wouldn't be bothered by snowdrifts down on the ground. Besides, living at the North Pole, the reindeer were used to lots of snow. My confidence in Santa was unshakable.

The situation became alarming when our parents assured us Santa would come when he could, but in the meantime, there were still family presents under our tree. Gloom settled over our house. I couldn't believe it! How could Santa Claus not come? My brothers often teased me, and I was sure this was just one of their jokes, but what if it was true? It couldn't be true. Santa would come; he loved me, and he would come.

Christmas Eve arrived, and I was the only one who still held any hope that Santa would come. I glared at my brothers each time they reminded me Santa couldn't make it this year. Surely they were wrong; Santa wouldn't disappoint me.

Three loud rings suddenly sounded from our long-silent telephone. It was our ring, but it didn't matter. In those party-line days, no matter whose ring it was, Daddy would have picked it up, just as we knew the half dozen neighbors who also heard the ring were lifting their receivers to their ears.

"Yes, this is Jed . . . Yes . . . Yes . . . Noon? I'll be there." There was a pause, then I knew Daddy was no longer talking to whoever had called but to the neighbors who had been listening in.

"As soon as I can get the horses harnessed. . . . I'll wait a few minutes if you aren't here by the time the horses are ready, Claude. . . . I'll go cross field to Courtney's place and meet you and Virgil there."

After a few more statements that made no sense to me, Daddy hung up the phone, picked up Mama, and twirled her around. The two of them disappeared into their bedroom for a few minutes, then Daddy came out wearing overalls over his jeans and two shirts. Mama fussed over a scarf around his neck as he fastened his heavy coat and pulled a cap over his ears.

"We need to get both teams harnessed!" He grinned at my brothers, and they scrambled into coats and boots. My brothers were back in a short time, and as they entered the house, I could hear the jangle of Ginger's, Snap's, King's, and Duke's harnesses and knew Daddy was taking the big wagon sled down the lane.

Something exciting was happening, but no one would tell me anything. My teenage brothers teased us younger kids mercilessly and seemed to be in a jovial mood. Mama smiled a lot, though she still frequently climbed on a chair to look out the window over the kitchen sink, and she often paused as though listening.

Evening had come, and the boys were preparing to start chores when Daddy arrived home. He handed Mama a thick stack of envelopes, and there were tears in her eyes as she hugged them to her. Silent messages seemed to fly back and forth between Mama and him. Chores were finished in record time, and Christmas cards fluttered from Mama's temporary clothesline. Soon we were gathered in the living room. Daddy read the Nativity story from St. Luke, and we exchanged simple presents. As usual, we girls were the recipients of a box of cherry chocolates from our three older brothers, and we gave them socks or something equally practical.

Then it was bedtime. We had no fancy felt stockings to hang and no fireplace, but each of us placed the biggest stocking we owned at the foot of our beds. Since we were encouraged to hang our stockings on the footboard, I felt pretty sure Santa Claus really was coming, and all of the earlier warnings really had been teasing to be forgotten.

Morning was slow in coming; it always was on Christmas. I have no memory of what Santa left under the tree, but I do remember the happiness and excitement. There was probably a doll and a book. Perhaps that was the year I got a little plastic bird whistle that warbled when it was filled with water. After all the gifts had been examined and tried out, I wandered into the kitchen and was surprised to see a pile of flattened cardboard boxes.

Many years passed, and I sat with Daddy, who was approaching his one hundredth birthday. Somehow his thoughts turned to that long-ago Christmas. He spoke of how worried he and Mama had been when one blizzard after another had piled up so much snow the county plows couldn't keep the highway open and they didn't even try to plow the country roads. Schools were closed, and the mailman couldn't get through. They didn't know how even Santa would make it through. And then the phone call had come from the postmaster in Arco. He'd heard Daddy had a big hay wagon on runners and proposed that if Daddy could get that hay wagon to the junction where our farm road met the highway by noon, he'd meet him there. The county had a plow ready to clear the highway from Arco to Moore, and the postmaster planned to follow it, hoping to meet farmers like Daddy at several points along the way. Farmers from all around the area had jumped into action in spite of another approaching storm.

With time and the revelation of Daddy's story, I suspected the reason for those Montgomery Ward boxes in our kitchen was that Santa's reindeer were exhausted from battling the wind and the snow. Santa did all he could, then Daddy and his big sleigh did the rest. Santa didn't let me down then or ever. Daddy's story simply confirmed what I'd always known: Santa Claus really did love me.

OTHER BOOKS AND AUDIO BOOKS
BY JENNIE HANSEN

*Abandoned*

*All I Hold Dear*

*Beyond Summer Dreams*

*The Bracelet*

*The Emerald*

*The Topaz*

*The Ruby*

*Breaking Point*

*Chance Encounter*

*Code Red*

*The Heirs of Southbridge*

*High Country*

*High Stakes*

*Macady*

*Run Away Home*

*Journey Home*

*Coming Home*

*Shudder*

*Some Sweet Day*

*When Tomorrow Comes*

*Wild Card*

*Where the River Once Flowed*

# Girbaud, Guess, and God

By Hank Smith

The year was 1992. Most everyone had seen Disney's latest film *Aladdin*, with the hilarious antics of Robin Williams, and we had a new president of the United States, a Southern man named Bill Clinton. But I didn't really care about politics or *Aladdin*, really; I was more concerned about Candace Cameron on ABC's sitcom *Full House*. She was gorgeous.

I was fourteen years old and in the middle of my eighth-grade year at Pine View Junior High School in a small but growing town in the southwest corner of Utah. There were many things in life I didn't know then, and I still don't know them today—things like the inner workings of quantum physics and the whys and hows of thermodynamics—but there is one thing I am totally and utterly sure of: junior high school was concocted in Satan's living room and built in his backyard.

Honestly, whose idea was junior high? Who was the lunatic who gave birth to this cesspool of anxiety and self-doubt? We take almost all of the most insecure people in society and put them together in one building for eight hours a day, five days a week, and don't even question the whole idea. We even buy our beloved young ones new clothes as we send them off to this land of overwhelming vulnerability, cruel bullying, and up-to-date temptation.

It was in that kind of junior high school land that I walked the halls with a fully brushed, blond, curly mullet. I was entirely sheathed in the 1990s. The hours I spent with my Sony Walkman made certain I had every Boyz II Men song memorized. I was overflowing with unearned confidence and was steadily working my way up the social pecking order, sacrificing old elementary school friendships with those who were now deemed too "uncool" in order to be crowned with the honor of becoming one of the popular kids. Yes, I was radical. Yes, I was da bomb. Yes, I was too legit to quit.

There was one thing that made me better than all of my peers. I owned the one thing that christened me as a king among the peasants. When I started school that year, my parents bought me a brand-new pair of Girbaud jeans. I had coveted those jeans from the moment I realized how they would propel me up the ladder of social significance. Those jeans cost my hardworking parents somewhere around seventy dollars. Could they afford to spend that kind of money on a single pair of pants? As if! But what did that matter? No sacrifice was too great for the accolades I would receive from the other nobles, aristocrats, and jocks when they saw the white Girbaud tag glimmering off the fabric that covered the fly. Those jeans were a mark of my superiority. I wore them with pride. When I put them on, I felt powerful. With my Girbaud jeans, I was all that and a bag of chips.

It was in the middle of all my social maneuvering that I came to a harsh realization. The jeans had done for me what no other piece of clothing before them had come close to doing—they were opening the door for my being dubbed "popular." But my social goals were being undermined by a simple fact that plagued my thoughts from the moment

I entered the school each day. The most popular students didn't simply wear Girbaud jeans; they also wore a shirt that, when combined with the jeans, a brown braided belt, and Air Jordans, made them socially unstoppable. The shirt came in two distinct styles. It was either adorned in horizontal stripes, alternating between solid white and a stripe of one color, such as blue or red, or it came in one solid color. Having a striped or nonstriped shirt made little difference as long as the wearer had the mark of royalty embroidered across the front of the shirt in all caps: GUESS JEANS, INC. A single shirt cost more than my jeans, but I absolutely had to have one. There was no question about it. I could no longer rely on my Hypercolor shirt to make me stand out. My parents might as well ask me to survive for a year without oxygen if they expected me to survive without a wicked awesome GUESS JEANS, INC. shirt.

Lucky for me, Christmas was quickly approaching. I saw this as the perfect opportunity for my parents to buy the shirt, and I was certain they would come through for me. I asked my mother about the shirt more and more as Christmas approached. With a GUESS JEANS, INC. shirt tucked into my Girbaud jeans, which were, of course, pegged around my ankles, I was sure to be catapulted to the top of Pine View Junior's social hierarchy.

I was blind to the lights, messages, spirit, and warmth of Christmas. For me, Christmas was about one thing: a GUESS JEANS, INC. shirt. I couldn't have been more excited. I would sit and smile through the endless holiday parties with family and friends, feel-good Christmas stories and movies, and traditional holiday songs—as long as it meant that when all was said and done, I would have that shirt. I had found the meaning of Christmas, and I was praying it would be under the tree on Christmas morning.

The day finally arrived. My family had stayed the night at my grandmother's house in Salt Lake like we had done every year since I could remember. As soon as the last person was awake, we gathered in the family room, each of us in our parachute pants. We had swollen faces and bed head. It was then that we began passing the presents from one person to another until everyone had a massive pile of colored boxes and ribbon displayed at their side. There were gasps of excitement from my sisters and some moans of complaint from my brothers as we opened each present one by one. As my pile of gifts began to dwindle, I found myself becoming nervous. Where was my shirt? My family had already given me many thoughtful gifts, but that didn't matter much to me. What did any of it matter if I didn't get what I really wanted? It was then that my mother pulled a perfectly wrapped gift out from behind her back. She handed it to me with a smile. She probably said something very sweet, but I was too busy taking in the realization of what was happening. Yes! Yes! Yes! I unwrapped that box faster than Billy Ray could sing "Achy Breaky Heart."

I'll never forget lifting the lid off the box and seeing the embroidered words. My heart skipped a beat. My mother had gone over and beyond the call of duty. For me, her favorite child, she had purchased a pure white GUESS JEANS, INC. shirt. I decided it was symbol of my "celestial" popularity. I was absolutely and completely elated. Christmas was a complete success.

Within seconds of opening the present, I had the shirt on. It fit perfectly. It was everything I had thought it would be. I was already picturing myself walking down the school hallway. Every girl would adore me, and every guy would envy me.

I was in heaven, and at that point, there was only one thing that could take my mind off of my new shirt: food.

My dad always made a huge Christmas breakfast after we opened our gifts, and the smell of scrambled eggs smothered in cheese snapped me back into reality. I quickly made my way out of the living room and into the kitchen before my siblings could beat me to the hot pancakes. As I sat down at the kitchen table, I poured myself a glass of grape juice and waited for my dad to fill my plate. As he did so, I picked up the juice to take a sip before digging in.

I have never been a coordinated person. The hours I spent on the Atari playing Donkey Kong never really gave me the agility and finesse I hoped they would.

As the glass hit my lips, I must have completely overestimated the size of my mouth. To be honest, I really don't know what happened. All I know is that the grape juice was intended for my stomach, and most of it made it there; however, a small amount, probably not more than a tablespoon, dripped out of the side of the glass, down my chin, and right onto the center of my brand-new pure white shirt.

I had literally opened the box ten minutes earlier, and now I sat in my grandmother's kitchen with a long purple stain directly in the middle of my shirt.

I didn't know what to say. Dumbfounded, I looked down at the stain and then up at my family, who hadn't noticed that in a matter of seconds my entire life had crumpled into oblivion. I calmly got up from the table and, when out of sight, ran panicked into the bathroom. I thought if I soaked the shirt under the water from the faucet the stain would disappear. I scrubbed and soaked, scrubbed and soaked. The stain didn't disappear. I appealed to my mother for help. Everything she and I tried that morning, from hairspray to vinegar to bleach couldn't entirely lift the three-inch purple line from the white fibers of the shirt. It stood out like the mole on Cindy Crawford's lip, and it was never going away.

The only hallway my shirt ever saw was the hallway of my grandmother's house. I never wore it to school. I never experienced the social glory I was certain it would have brought me. It sat in my closet and only came out when I needed to mow the lawn or paint the fence.

Fast forward twenty-two years.

I'm sitting in my own home at the kitchen counter, typing away at my laptop in a blue T-shirt, white gym shorts, and dark black dress socks. I stopped thinking about fashion a long time ago. My five children are all asleep, and my wife is reading a book over by the Christmas tree. Every single popular movie, clothing brand, musician, and celebrity from my teenage years was replaced by a new one, and that one was replaced by another one, and that one by another one. (Although I hear you can pick up a pair of used Girbaud jeans on eBay for around five dollars.)

The siblings I unwrapped presents with each Christmas are now parents themselves. My mom and dad, who carted me around during the holidays, are now grandparents. My Girbaud jeans and the two other GUESS JEANS, INC. shirts my mother bought for me after my grape juice mishap have all been thrown away or donated to charity.

My attitude and outlook on life has changed. Instead of worrying about looking good, I worry about being good. I want opportunity more than I want popularity, and I hope for greater spirituality more than greater superiority. The things I used to feel were crucial to my happiness I now look upon as superficial. In fact, there is almost nothing about my life today that resembles my life as a teenager.

Except Him. I didn't notice or understand the Savior's subtle hand in my life then, but I can see it now. He was patient and kind as He allowed me to learn the lessons of life, sometimes the hard way. He saw me not just as the fickle teen I was but for the man I could become. Instead of seeing a superficial child, He saw potential.

I now worry more about spiritual stains than physical stains. Each Christmas, I celebrate my chance to completely eliminate any spiritual stains and become pure again. The commemoration of the birth of the Son of God reminds me of the eternal and unchanging love Christ showed through His Atonement. The stain on my shirt never came out, but there is no stain that can't be completely cleansed and purified by the power and majesty of our Savior.

# One Fowl Christmas

BY GALE SEARS

"You're an odd child," my mother said to me. "You want to serve what for Christmas dinner?"

"Goose," I repeated unabashedly. I was eight that Christmas (1959), and I'd just finished watching Dickens's *A Christmas Carol.* The story had so completely transported me to the environs of England that I was speaking to everyone in a cockney accent and longing for plum pudding and the Cratchet's Christmas goose. Though the goose in the film was small, it looked absolutely delicious, and I wanted to sink my teeth into one.

My mom stood at the kitchen sink washing the breakfast dishes. She gave me a sidelong look. "And where do you expect me to find a goose?"

She did our major grocery shopping every Thursday, so I thought her question rather dumb. "At the grocery store," I answered, trying not to sound cheeky.

Mother stopped washing dishes. I thought she was angry, but then I saw a slight smile at the corner of her mouth. "At *our* grocery store?"

Was this a trick question? "Yes," I said after pausing to be sure this truly was the answer I wanted to give.

She chuckled and shook her head. "At the Al Tahoe market?"

I stood firm. "Yes. Why are you laughing?"

"You certainly keep life interesting," she said, setting the final glass in the drainer and wiping her hands on the tea towel. She sat with me at the kitchen table. "Now, I'm going to be serious about this because I think you're serious."

Of course I was serious! Hadn't she seen that lovely Christmas goose being borne proudly to the table by Mrs. Cratchet? My mom normally went along with my creative requests, so I was thinking that perhaps she'd eaten goose and it hadn't tasted as lovely as it looked. "Doesn't goose taste good?" I asked hesitantly, not wanting a negative reply.

"Heavens, I don't know. I've never eaten it."

I sighed in relief. "Well then, what's the problem?"

"My dearest daughter, we live in South Lake Tahoe, California."

"So?"

"We have three small markets."

I shifted in my seat and glanced out at the thickly falling snow, then I looked back at her and shrugged. "So?"

"It's my guess that none of them will have a goose for us to cook for Christmas."

"Really?"

"Really. None of them have the space in their stores to carry a lot of fancy stuff."

"Is goose fancy?"

"Very fancy." Mom stood and took off her apron.

I stared at the flowers on her dress, attempting to keep silly tears out of my eyes. Oh, how I'd set my heart on that *Christmas Carol* goose!

Mom must have discerned the look on my face because she came over and patted my shoulder. "Tell you what. I'll take you around to the markets tomorrow, and you can ask them if they have any geese for sale."

I brightened immediately. "Really?"

"Yes, but you'll have to speak with the store managers yourself. It will be *your* project."

I nodded enthusiastically. "Yes, ma'am."

* * *

When my two older sisters discovered what I was planning, they were less than supportive.

Vicki was in junior high school and was hypersensitive to anything out of the norm. She assaulted my mom with drama. "A goose for Christmas dinner? Is she kidding? That is so weird! I'm not eating goose for Christmas dinner. I'll go over to my friend's house, where they have normal food. Who in the world eats goose for Christmas dinner? Where did she come up with such a crazy idea? Can't you just make her go live with the neighbors?"

My sister Teri took a more logical approach. "Nobody wants crummy goose for Christmas dinner, Mom. And besides, Betty Lawson is coming for dinner, and she's very finicky about what she eats, isn't she?"

I wondered why Teri was using Betty Lawson in her argument. She didn't even like the little silver-haired lady. Mrs. Lawson was my parents' friend. She owned a lodge and cluster of rustic cabins that had housed Tahoe tourists since the 1920s. My dad called her a scrappy pioneer. She was very opinionated and belonged to a religion that didn't believe in doctors or sickness. She had come for dinner once when Teri was sick with the measles and had stated flatly that she wasn't really sick—that it was all in her mind. Teri had declared Mrs. Lawson to be *out* of *her* mind, and the two had been at odds ever since.

My mom ignored my sisters' harangues. On Saturday afternoon, she and I bundled up in our warmest clothes and went out in a snowstorm to search for a goose. It was lovely driving slowly along in our 1952 Ford sedan. Mom was humming a Nat King Cole Christmas song while the windshield wipers chanted, "You will find goose, you will find goose, you will find goose." I stared out the windshield into the wider world. There had to be a goose out there somewhere.

Mom pulled to a stop in front of the Al Tahoe market, and I took a deep breath. I sat for a moment with my gloved fingers wrapped around the door handle. I was a daring girl, yet I had to admit I was a little nervous about talking to the store manager about my "fancy" request. What if he laughed at me or didn't understand what I was talking about?

*"You want a what?"*

*"A goose. You know, like in the* Christmas Carol *movie?"*

"Never saw it."

"Oh."

"We have chickens or turkeys or hams but no geese. Where do you think you are, San Francisco?"

Mom gave me an encouraging look. "You okay?"

I nodded and slipped from the car. Before I closed the door, Mom said, "Mr. Sullivan's a nice man. He'll help you if he can."

I jumped when Margaret, at checkout, yelled Mr. Sullivan's name across the small store. She popped her gum and smiled at me until Mr. Sullivan arrived. I wished she'd go stock shelves or something so she wouldn't overhear my little prepared speech.

"How can I help you?" Mr. Sullivan asked.

I'd never actually spoken to him, but I'd seen him around the store a lot. He was a thin man with gray hair and dark-framed glasses. His two front teeth sort of poked out from under his lip, but I tried not to stare at them.

"Hi, Mr. Sullivan. I want my mom to cook a goose for Christmas, and I was wondering if you had one?" Oops!

That wasn't in my prepared speech. "I . . . I don't mean you; I meant your store. Does your store have any geese, or a goose? One goose will do."

Margaret's eyebrows went up, and I saw a laugh twitch the corners of her mouth. I glanced back at Mr. Sullivan, who was not laughing but, instead, looking over my head. I turned quickly, expecting to see a space with penned-up geese, but no, it was only a display of Jell-O pudding and pound cake.

"Geese, eh? For Christmas?"

"Yes, sir."

I was hoping his next word wouldn't be *weird*.

He took off his glasses and squinted at me. "Hmm. Can't say as I've ever had a request for goose."

*So, do you have one or not?* I wondered anxiously. He cleaned his glasses on his store coat and put them back on. *Come on, Mr. Sullivan! This isn't the sixty-four-million-dollar question!*

"Nope, sorry, little girl. We don't carry geese, and I'm afraid there's not enough time before Christmas to order one from San Francisco. We only get a shipment every two weeks."

"Oh . . . okay. Thanks," I stammered.

Margaret gave me a "boy, are you weird" look as I backed toward the door.

"Okay, thanks," I said again, pasting a fake smile on my face. I pushed out into the snowstorm and headed for the car, giving myself a pep talk. *Oh well, there are still two more stores to go, and surely one of them will be smart enough to have something more original for Christmas than turkey or ham.*

But Mr. Blair at the Bijou market stopped just long enough in hanging up the huge jolly cardboard Santa to say, "No can do."

Things were getting desperate. One more store to go. One more hope for the dream to come true. Mom and I were quiet as we traveled to Cecile's market. Now the windshield wipers were saying, "*C sells market is the last chance, C sells market is the last chance.*" Between the swishing wiper voices, I silently offered a little prayer. I was used to the every night "Now I lay me down to sleep" version, so coming up with something original was a bit like trying to understand fractions, but I needed all the help I could get, so I gave it a try. *Um, uh . . .* I prayed silently. *Uh . . . I don't guess people had Christmas goose when you were born in that little stable, but maybe they did 'cause there were chickens and stuff, and there could have been a goose. Anyway, my mom said that people were glad when you were born 'cause you would do a lot of good things for them. And I would be awful glad if we could find just one small goose and have a different sort of Christmas this year. The end—I mean, amen.*

"Third time's a charm!" Mom said as she pulled the car into Cecile's small parking lot. "Want me to come in with you? You've never been inside this market."

I wanted to be up to the task. "No, thanks. I can do it."

"Okay. Cecile Marconi is the owner, and he's also a butcher, so if anyone can help you, he can."

I loved my mom—always so positive. I nodded and got out of the car. There was quite a bit of snow on the street now, so I fit my boots into the footprints of someone else who had ventured out before me. I climbed the steps up to the market entrance, took a deep breath, and shoved open the door. Once inside, I looked around for Mr. Marconi. My eyes took in the shelves lined with the usual soup, cereal, and toothpaste, but I also saw unusual stuff: boxes of funny-looking spaghetti, bread in weird shapes, and long strings of sausages hung over the butcher's counter.

"Excuse me," I said to the dark-haired man behind the counter. He looked at me and smiled. "I'm looking for Mr. Marconi, the owner."

"That's me!" the man returned.

I took off my gloves and got down to business. "I want to have goose for Christmas this year. Does your store have any of those?"

Mr. Marconi came out from behind the meat counter. "Christmas goose, like they have over in England?"

I caught my breath. "Yes! Just like in the movie. That English movie."

Mr. Marconi's eyes twinkled. "Ah, *A Christmas Carol.*"

"Yes!" My little eight-year-old heart was promising to pray a lot more.

"No, I'm sorry, little one. I don't have any Christmas geese in my store."

"Oh," was all I could say as the smile dropped off my face and crashed to the floor. "Oh, okay." I pulled the gloves from my coat pocket and turned to leave.

"But, maybe . . ."

I stopped.

"Maybe I can find one for you."

I turned back. "Really?"

"Sure, we can try. I'm not promising anything, but I'm going down to Sacramento a few days before Christmas for supplies. I'll look around—see what I can find."

"Thank you! Thank you so much!" I turned to race out and tell my mom the great news.

"Hey! Wait a minute," Mr. Marconi yelled after me. "Who are you?"

I stopped, and we laughed together. "I'm Gale. My mom is Elaine, and my dad is Norman . . . Kamp."

Mr. Marconi nodded. "Oh yeah. I know your dad. He does my taxes."

"Yep, that's the one. Thanks again, Mr. Marconi."

I heard him chuckling as I ran out of the store.

"He's going to try to find us a goose, Mom!" I yelled excitedly as I climbed into the car. "It's not for sure, but he's gonna try!"

Mom put the car into gear and backed out of the parking lot. "You certainly keep life interesting," she said.

The words reached over and hugged me.

\* \* \*

That Christmas, Mr. Marconi was Santa Claus for me. And even though he brought the goose over Echo Summit in his beat-up red truck, it might just as well have been a sleigh pulled by eight reindeer. My sisters tried to keep up the façade of irritation about the goose, but when they sat down with Mom and me at the kitchen table Christmas morning to look for a goose-cooking recipe, I knew they were almost as wound up as I was. We watched Mom as she ran her finger down the index columns.

"Gingerbread, gingersnaps, glazed carrots, gooseberry pie—"

"Well?" Vicki asked, trying not to sound anxious.

"Ah. Goose," my mom said triumphantly, flipping the pages to the appropriate place. "This *Better Homes and Gardens* cookbook has never let me down." She wiggled her fingers at us. "Now, you three vamoose until I need your help with potato mashing, bean cooking, setting the table, and entertaining Mrs. Lawson."

"Count me out on that last job," Teri grumbled.

\* \* \*

The table was lovely. Mom draped it with an embossed white tablecloth, Dad carefully carried out Great-Grand-mother's heirloom china and crystal goblets, and Mrs. Lawson furnished a pine-bough-and-cranberry centerpiece. The high-handed little woman also supplied bossy instructions on how to set the table, as well as a baked chicken, yams, and sourdough rolls.

"I am not about to eat a greasy old goose at my age," she snapped.

Her crankiness could not get me down. As mother came from the kitchen carrying the honored Christmas goose, I felt as though I had, for just a moment, fallen into the pages of Mr. Dickens's story. I'm sure the others did not feel the thrill of the moment, but to me it was magical. Mother was Mrs. Cratchet, Father was kind, hardworking Mr. Cratchet, and Mrs. Lawson was . . . Scrooge. I giggled at the thought. We all cheered and clapped as my mother set the goose on the table.

My father raised his goblet. "To Christmas!" he said loudly.

"To Christmas!" we all echoed.

"God bless us, everyone!" my mother said, winking at me.

"Especially the strange ones who want goose for Christmas," Mrs. Lawson croaked.

We all looked at her in stunned silence for a moment, and then we burst into laughter—laughter that filled our home and spilled out into the snowy Tahoe night.

It is treasured laughter that has rung in my memory for many years.

OTHER BOOKS AND AUDIO BOOKS
BY GALE SEARS

*Autumn Sky*

*Until the Dawn*

*Upon the Mountains*

*Christmas for a Dollar*

*The Missing Christmas Treasure*

# The Perfect Christmas

BY JENNIFER MOORE

"James, honey, don't touch the Christmas decorations," I told my two-year-old son for what seemed like the hundredth time. I moved him out of the way and rearranged my beautiful olive-wood Nativity on the coffee table, making sure to return each figurine to its exact position to balance out the grouping: Mary and Joseph in the middle, next to the manger; Wise Men on one side; and shepherds on the other. Luckily, there were a few sheep to keep it symmetrical. I turned one or two and straightened the table runner they sat on.

Holding on to James's hand, I helped his chubby finger point to the different characters as I told him the names and listened to his young voice and stilted words as he repeated them back as well as he could. When I pointed to the infant lying in the carved wooden hay, James said, "Baby Jesus" before I prompted him, and I made a mental tally mark on my list of things to do to create the perfect Christmas.

Teach child the true meaning of Christmas. Check.

I picked James up and carried him out of the living room, reminding him that this room wasn't for playing. I glanced around quickly to make sure he hadn't disturbed anything else in my magazine-perfect decorated house. I headed off to find something to distract him and keep him away from the Christmas decorations.

This would be the first year my husband and I weren't
making the drive from Cedar City to Salt Lake a few days
before Christmas to attend all of the family parties and to
spend Christmas morning at one of our parents' houses. We'd
decided that *we'd* be the parents this year and have our very
first Christmas at home to establish our own traditions and
memories.

As the young mother of two-year-old James and three-
month-old Ben, I was determined to make it the most
perfect season ever. We'd put lights on the house in October
before the first big snowstorm, and I'd hung a wreath with
hand-sewn plush snowmen on our door after Halloween.

The day after Thanksgiving, we'd assembled and decorated
a brand-new Christmas tree, upon which we'd hung our yearly
"special" ornaments. Beneath the tree, gifts waited, covered in
coordinating wrapping paper and tied with elaborate bows.
CDs of holiday music rotated on a two-and-a-half-day basis
so we would be able to hear all of them, and I figured out
that if we watched one Christmas movie every other night,
we would make it through my stack of VHS tapes before
Christmas Day.

I'd worked tirelessly for weeks, sewing a tree skirt to
match the tea towels hanging on the oven door and the
throw blanket arranged on the back of the sofa. With
each family member in mind, I'd chosen our stockings
carefully, and they now dangled from pegs in the family
room, precisely six-and-a-half inches apart. The house
smelled like a blend of pine- and cinnamon-scented Yankee
candles. Christmas quilts and pillowcases adorned each
bed, and garlands and bows ensconced every shelf, railing,
windowsill, and doorframe.

The perfect Christmas would take a little extra work,
but it would be worth it when we looked back at all the
amazing memories we were making.

A few days after the Nativity incident with my son and a flurry of holiday activities later, I was in the kitchen mixing up icing for gingerbread houses when I again heard the sound of the wooden figures sliding across the coffee table. I wiped my hands on my Christmas apron and hurried into the living room. James was moving the Nativity around again, and there was a crumpled piece of toilet paper draped across baby Jesus. I looked around, relieved that nothing else was out of place. Lifting James out of the way, I repositioned the figures and picked up the scrap of toilet paper. Play group would arrive at any moment, and I still needed to get all of the gingerbread-house candies ready.

I plopped James on the counter, where I could keep an eye on him, and scolded him again for playing in the living room. I reminded him that the Christmas decorations weren't toys.

As we completed one activity, my mind was already racing to the next. Lists and planning and preparations were keeping us organized. The holiday season was rolling like a well-oiled machine.

I was even ready with family home evenings to last the entire month, complete with treat, activity, lesson, and song. My Young Women class had planned service projects; I'd made treats enclosed in cellophane and ribbon for my husband's office. I had gifts arranged in a fabric-lined basket on a table inside the front door for my visiting teaching ladies, the Nursery leaders, and my husband's home teaching families, and homemade jam wrapped and tagged for our neighbors sat in a basket next to the gifts.

I'd purchased matching sweaters from Baby Gap months earlier for James and Ben and had taken pictures of them in front of the tree to include in our family letter. I'd mailed the cards on December 1 and followed them a week later with the packages we were sending to relatives.

We'd been to the Christmas lighting ceremony on Main Street, written letters to Santa, and driven up to Leigh Hill to see the light display and get a candy cane, but there was still plenty more Christmas celebrating ahead. If we were going to do every single thing on the list, we needed to stick to our schedule.

The Saturday before Christmas, our day started early. After updating our three advent calendars, I dressed the kids in matching outfits, hurried to check Walmart and Kmart just to see if any Tickle Me Elmos had come in the night before, then drove down to St. George to get the kids' pictures taken with Santa at the mall. We were all exhausted, but the ward Christmas party that night would be so marvelous we couldn't miss it.

Some of the stakes in Cedar City had pooled their Christmas-party money and, in a warehouse by the airport, had built a set that looked like a small Jewish town. The wards took turns having their Christmas parties in "Bethlehem." The young men dressed up as Roman centurions, we all had "coins" to pay our taxes and buy dinner, and everyone was supposed to come in costume.

I'd glued the invitation for the party in our Christmas scrapbook and had surrounded it with die cuts of a Middle-Eastern cityscape, a Christmas star, and palm trees. A rectangular piece of sand-colored paper measuring exactly four-and-a-half by six-and-a-half inches waited to frame the picture of our family at "Back to Bethlehem" night. Even though my husband was out of town, I was still determined to complete the page with the perfect picture of my boys and me in our costumes.

I wore a bedsheet over my shoulder and tied around my waist with a belt, and covered my hair in a scarf. Ben was easy to wrap in blankets, and then I turned my efforts to James, who had fallen asleep on the stairs.

I woke him up and put him in his bathrobe, but when I tried to tie a pillowcase around his head with a strip of fabric, it was too much, and he started to cry (though anyone who has had a two-year-old knows that *cry* is a mild term). I decided to worry about the pillowcase when we got to the party.

Simply put, that night was a disaster. Sitting on a cement floor, trying to juggle a colicky newborn and a two-year-old who was melting down at the idea of eating pita bread, hummus, and olives was a low point, to say the least. Realizing I hadn't even remembered my camera and knowing this tantrum was only going to get worse, I folded the blanket, and the three of us left the party, worn out and frustrated.

James was too wound up to fall asleep, so I sat him on the couch to calm him down while he watched *Elmo Saves Christmas*, even though it was out of order in the VHS stack.

Just as Elmo and Santa were singing "Keep Christmas with You All through the Year," I put the cinnamon rolls and wassail for Sunday morning into the fridge and went to get James. It was hours past bedtime, and we still had to tear a ring off his paper chain and read a Christmas story.

James wasn't on the couch, where I'd left him.

I heard the scrape of wood, and the irritation that I'd felt all evening surfaced. The night had been ruined, and I was completely drained. I closed my eyes. This wasn't going to be pretty.

I stormed up the stairs to the living room. When I reached the doorway, I drew in a breath to unleash my anger, but what I saw stopped me cold, and my heart felt like it had been smashed in the Grinch's measuring device. I remember the scene as clearly as if it had happened a moment ago.

In the glow of the Christmas-tree lights, James was carefully pushing all the wooden figures closer together until they surrounded the baby Jesus in a tight circle, and he was saying their names in toddler grunts that only moms understand. He lifted the baby from the manger and, with his chubby hands, clumsily wrapped a piece of toilet paper around the mostly naked, little carved body, rocking him and humming a tuneless song before carefully setting him back down.

I stood stunned in one of those moments of clarity, where it was like someone had handed me a new pair of glasses and suddenly the world looked different. My gaze moved around my perfect house to the tree and the quilted throw pillows, the nutcracker on the piano, the bows, the garland. Everything suddenly seemed garish and excessive.

I lifted James onto my lap, and we sat on the sofa quietly as the Christmas spirit filled the room. The *real* Christmas Spirit. The very thing I'd tried to create through months of planning and hours upon hours of work. The feeling was something that couldn't be manufactured. It was as simple as just sitting quietly.

I'd discovered what had been missing from our perfect Christmas: time to actually remember why we celebrate Christmas in the first place. It wasn't a chance to show decorating skills or the ability to find the perfect gift. Christmas wasn't about making traditions just for the sake of crossing them off the list. I felt squirmy, a little sick, and a lot ashamed as I considered the past few months and how seldom I had actually remembered Christ as a part of my perfect Christmas.

The next day, I helped James choose fabric to make a blankie for the wooden baby Jesus, just as we had a few months earlier for his little brother, Ben. I cringed inside when he picked blue fabric with a pink floral pattern but took a calming breath and cut it into a small rectangle, which he carefully tucked around the little figure.

In a book, this story would wrap up neatly. This is where I'd say that I immortalized the moment by snapping a picture and putting it in the "Bethlehem" page of the Christmas scrapbook or how, from that day forward, I learned my lesson and the holidays have been calm and easy ever since, but neither of those is true.

I did learn something though. And sixteen years later, that experience still rates among one of the most dear to my heart. Every year at Christmastime, I pull out that mangy scrap of ugly fabric and place it on baby Jesus to remind me of the moment when a two-year-old taught me a powerful lesson—the lesson *I* should have taught *him*. He showed me the importance of slowing down and being grateful. And even though traditions can be distracting, when our hearts are in the right place, traditions make the holidays special and help facilitate the Christmas spirit.

Elder James Moore is spending his first Christmas away from home this year, serving the Lord as a missionary. I know he is sharing the same Spirit he felt as a little boy and is teaching the people in the Washington Everett Mission that the greatest Christmas traditions of all are also the simplest and center around our Savior's love.

# Of Walls and Trees

## BY SHAUNA HUMPHREYS

In November 1989, the Berlin Wall came down, a momentous and historically significant global event that changed lives and altered the course of European history. That same year, our Christmas tree came down—several days *before* Christmas. In the global scheme of things, this didn't warrant even as much as a nanoblip on history's radar; however, it caused a considerable ripple on what, to that point, had seemed to be the smooth surface of our family's Christmas preparations.

I mention the Berlin Wall because in 1989 my son Danny was enrolled in a six-month Brigham Young University study-abroad program based in Austria, and he was privileged to witness firsthand this fallen edifice and even brought home a small handful of its rocky remains. Along with the rest of the world, our family was fascinated and excited by this impressive event that would finally allow families and friends who had long been separated to be reunited; we were equally excited at the prospect of our very own family reunion as we anticipated Danny's return home shortly before Christmas.

Like all moms, I wanted everything to be just right, so while juggling life as a single parent, graduate classes at BYU with their looming finals, and the rigors of teaching freshman composition, I worked feverishly (and even pulled a few all-nighters) to bake all our favorite treats and make sure the

house was squeaky clean and tastefully decorated for the
holiday season. The crowning touch was the Christmas tree
(an artificial beauty that required considerable assembly). At
that time, trees were not prelit, so when I finally felt I had the
tree looking plump and perky enough, I began the arduous
job of arranging the strings of tiny, brightly colored lights,
a task that always looked so idyllic in Christmas movies
but which, in my case, was always somewhat daunting and
invariably left me feeling hot and frazzled rather than warm and
fuzzy. How was it possible to end up with incompatible plug
endings? With me, it seemed to be a special talent! However,
after several false starts and failed attempts, I was finally able
to connect the strings of lights correctly, and the tree fairly
dazzled (in some spots more than others). If I stood back and
sort of squinted, the uneven distribution of lights was barely
discernible, and I gave myself a figurative pat on my aching
back. As was our family tradition, once the tree was decorated,
someone had to declare that it was perfectly beautiful and
beautifully perfect, and Danny's older sister, Tamara, made the
happy pronouncement, agreeing that her brother would come
home to a grand and glorious sight. Michelle, my seventeen-
year-old, just nodded pleasantly while giving her shoulders
the tiniest and almost imperceptible shrug.

The Salt Lake airport reunion was great, except for the fact
that Danny's sisters and I didn't recognize him at first because
he had opted for a longer hairstyle while he'd been away.
Fortunately, he recognized *us*, and we had a good chuckle
over our momentary lapse. I could hardly wait for us to get
back home to Orem and our cozy Christmas scenario; I was
sure Danny would hardly be able to restrain his cool, reserved,
eighteen-year-old excitement. And yes, he was suitably
impressed with it all—except for the tree, which garnered only
a noncommittal "hmmm" and a furtive exchange of glances

with Michelle, which puzzled me but was soon forgotten as the headlong rush of exams and grading and Christmas shopping consumed every last speck of my time and energy.

Then, at last (oh, happy day), exams were over, and grades were submitted, and as I pulled into our driveway with just a few days to spare and a handful of last-minute errands to run before Christmas, something caught my eye. At first I thought I was hallucinating; I was sure all of my scrambling and juggling of tasks and responsibilities had finally tossed me right over the edge. I'd seen it happen in the movies, read about it in books, and now I was personally plunged into this precarious predicament. And what did I imagine I was seeing? Why, it was nothing other than our plump and perky fake Christmas tree, complete with its strings of tiny multicolored lights, lying prone in our front yard. No doubt about it; I had come completely unglued.

Now, I'm not one to go down in flames without a valiant struggle, so I put my head down on the steering wheel and gave myself a swift and firm no-nonsense command to pull myself together. And when I lifted my head and opened my eyes . . . the tree was still there. I slowly got out of my car, walked across the snow-covered lawn, and knelt beside my fallen friend, gingerly touching its branches, a tactile testament that this was no hallucination. I went limp with relief and gratitude that I hadn't gone mad.

However, my relief soon gave way to complete consternation. How had this happened, and why? Who would do such a dastardly deed? The fall of a wall was one thing, but the fall of a Christmas tree was quite another. I hoped I would be able to restore this maligned pine to its rightful and upright position. And what about the children? Had they already witnessed this travesty? Were they numb with grief and shock, completely traumatized by this vile act of vandalism? Stumbling into the house, I knew I had to be strong, calm, comforting, and reassuring for their sake. How hideous would it be for them to find me babbling incoherently? I steeled myself for the task ahead as I mustered the courage to face the unsightly void where our trusty tannenbaum had once stood so proudly.

But there was no gaping hole. Instead, what to my wondering eyes should appear but a round, robust, aromatic, and authentic Christmas tree, alive and well and festooned with dozens of tiny clear lights symmetrically spaced and twinkling merrily—almost as merrily as the eyes of Danny and Michelle, who stood nearby, serenely satisfied with themselves and the tree. They stopped just short of a self-congratulatory "Ta-da!" complete with outstretched arms and tossing manes (Danny had not yet gotten a haircut, and Michelle's long blonde locks were legendary). And I had to admit, if somewhat deep down in my heart, just a tad grudgingly that they had done a spectacular job. After all, what mother wants to concede without a few regrets that after years of being the "Christmas tree queen" she has just been upstaged by her fledgling apprentices? They hastened to explain that in their humble, teenaged opinion (and I quote), "A fake tree with gaudy colored lights just isn't cool." During his pre-Christmas European travels, Danny had seen many beautifully decorated trees, all of which were the real thing and most of which were illuminated with clear, shiny lights. Apparently, he had shared this observation with Michelle, resulting in what they regarded as a sound, unanimous, executive decision to restore an aesthetically pleasing authenticity to our Christmas décor. So pooling their resources, they had found the "perfect" tree, hauled it home, and festooned it with what they deemed to be appropriate illumination after pitching out the offensive imposter. Once again, it fell to Tamara to declare the new tree to be beautiful.

As I sidled over to the living room window to furtively check on the hapless, homeless, forlorn tree lying in the front yard, the perfect solution for its brighter future suddenly occurred to me. I dashed to the phone, dialed my daughter Beki, and told her the great news. She and her husband, Dean, were now the proud owners of a fully (albeit somewhat haphazardly) lit, truly "ever green" tree. Being newly married and on a very tight budget, they had decided they could not afford a Christmas tree and would forgo that luxury. But suddenly, all they needed to do was drive by my house and literally pick one up. My dear old tree's fall from favor had become their windfall (no pun intended). Talk about winning the Christmas-tree lottery! Beki was hard-pressed to believe my story about what had happened, but seeing was believing, and before long, our old tree was zooming off to greener and kinder, gentler pastures. It gave new meaning to the old saying, "A Christmas tree lying down on a lawn is a lot cheaper than one standing up in a Boy Scout sales lot." I'm not sure that is *really* an old saying, but somebody kind of old just said it. Close enough!

Once we got past the aftershocks, this was to become a journal-entry Christmas. Danny had brought home some very thoughtful ethnic gifts and goodies for everyone, and he and I had the time of our lives helping Santa long after everyone else had gone to bed on Christmas Eve. We wrapped all the gifts and tucked them beneath the boughs of our new favorite tree, ready and waiting for what turned out to be a splendid Christmas morning. How we all enjoyed the spicy German gingerbread cookies (Pfeffernüsse); the melt-in-your-mouth chocolate treats, unsurpassed in their creamy, European decadence; special rings from Israel with our names engraved in Hebrew; colorful shopping bags from France; and my personal favorite, which I will treasure always: an old, leather-bound *Girls' Grammar School Shakespeare.*

Many Christmases and many trees (some artificial but mostly the real thing, and *always* adorned with clear, shiny lights) have come and gone since then, and our Danny is also gone, cut down in his prime by cancer. Yet there is never a Christmas when we don't remember him, miss him, and fondly recount precious memories, our favorite being the year of the tossed-out tree. Each year as I plug in the tiny, clear, twinkling lights, I am reminded of the tradition that began on that extraordinary Christmas past. I am reminded also of the clear and pure light that heralded the birth of our Savior Jesus Christ on that night of nights long ago and far away in a lowly manger. And I am humbly reminded of His wondrous words, "I am the light of the world: he that followeth me shall not walk in darkness, but shall have the light of life" (John 8:12). Many years ago, the Savior's clear and pure light guided Danny safely home from Austria to a loving family, and a few short years later, it guided him safely home again to that loving God who gave him life. The Savior's light penetrates the veil that temporarily separates loved ones, and by the gift of His light, our walls of loss and regret become monuments of hope, contentment, and healing—memorials to bright and tender memories, testaments of treasured times together, past, present, and future.

OTHER BOOKS
BY SHAUNA HUMPHREYS

*100 Favorite Verses from the Book of Mormon*

*100 Favorite Verses to Bring You Closer to Christ*

*100 Favorite Verses for Women*

*100 Favorite Verses for Missionaries*

*The Lord Is My Light: 365 Inspiring Verses
from the New Testament*

# Jesus Has a Nub Like Me

BY BRENT L. TOP

We have a grandson who was born with a birth defect. The lower part of his left arm and hand did not properly develop in utero. He and his family refer to his short arm and undeveloped hand as his "nub." Although it doesn't slow him down very much and he certainly doesn't consider himself handicapped, he does notice that he is different from others. He is at the age where he is conscious of the stares and unkind comments about his nub, and on one occasion, Gavin tearfully told his mom he wanted two hands like all of his friends. His "thorn in the flesh" was starting to become emotionally hard to bear—both for him and for all of us who love him and want the best for him. We hurt when he hurts. We feel badly when he feels badly.

In decorating her home for Christmas one year, our daughter Tiffany put out the olive-wood Nativity set we had given her as a Christmas gift when we'd lived in Israel many years before. It had taken a few hits and dings through the years and the family's many moves. There were a few chips and dents and a piece broken off here and there. One day, three-year-old Gavin excitedly exclaimed, "Mommy, look! Jesus has a nub just like me!" Part of one of the carved wooden arms of the baby Jesus had broken off. Nobody knew when the damage had occurred. It was so small that none of us had even noticed. Yet Gavin had noticed. He was thrilled that Jesus had a nub too. His mother explained to him that Jesus didn't really have a nub but that He understood exactly what it was like for Gavin to have one.

In that tender teaching moment, she once again taught him about the Resurrection and how Jesus's Atonement ensures that someday Gavin will have two hands and arms like everyone else.

That satisfied him. "That's okay, Mommy," Gavin said. "I like my nub. I'll keep it forever."

What Gavin had seen as a handicap—as a burden, an embarrassment—he now saw from a much different perspective. He was able to deal with his challenge better because he understood, even as a three-year-old, that Jesus understands what it is like to have a nub and that He will help Gavin throughout his life and someday give him a glorified body with the arm and hand that were missing in mortality.

Just as Gavin rejoiced in Jesus having a nub like him, we all long to know that Jesus understands us, relates to us personally, and can succor us in our own unique challenges and thorns in the flesh. We all want to have Jesus a little more like us so we can trust that He really knows our pains and understands our weaknesses.

One of the great messages of the Christmas season is the "condescension of God" (1 Nephi 11:16–18)—that the Great I Am came from His throne on high to be born in a humble stable in a relatively obscure Judean village. The Babe of Bethlehem was born as one of us so He can succor and strengthen us in our own unique challenges of life. As one of us, Jesus knows exactly what it is like to be every one of us. He knows us personally. He knows about Gavin's nub, and He knows about each of our struggles and what pains afflict us, because He experienced it all when He descended below all things (see D&C 122:8).

"And he shall go forth, suffering pains and afflictions and temptations of every kind; and this that the word might be fulfilled which saith he will take upon him the pains and the sicknesses of his people.

"And he will take upon him . . . their infirmities, that his bowels may be filled with mercy, according to the flesh, that he may know . . . how to succor his people according to their infirmities" (Alma 7:11–12).

## OTHER BOOKS AND AUDIO PRODUCTS AUTHORED
## OR COAUTHORED BY BRENT L. TOP

*Glimpses beyond Death's Door*

*Protecting Against Eternal Identity Theft*

# The Gift

By Richard J. Allen

*Every good gift and every perfect gift is from above,
and cometh down from the Father of lights.* (James 1:17)

Excitement filled the air. It was as if an unexpected Chinook wind had blown in with its welcome warmness to melt away the frigid frost and snow covering our Southern Alberta landscape. What was the sunny news? Our mother had decided to return early from her trip to California! She could not bear the thought of spending Christmas away from her family. In a warm letter, she expressed her longing to come home: "Christmas dinner with my family in my own home would make me very happy—just our own family, us four, no more. Maybe the cats. How about it?"

My sister, Shirley, and I were thrilled. Our father was too—but not without a sense of concern. As with previous pregnancies, my mom was having some recurring health difficulties and consequently had journeyed to Los Angeles in September so her brother, a celebrated obstetrician and gynecologist whose patients included a number of Hollywood stars, could treat her.

"As if with foreboding," my father wrote in his autobiography, "I felt impressed to advise her to spend the next few months in Los Angeles under [her brother's] care." Despite these anxieties, Mother returned to us in November. We were all filled with joy. Her emotion about the homecoming showed in a letter she wrote to one of her sisters shortly before Christmas:

*I am feeling much better than I did. Oh, it seemed so good to be home again with my family. And were they glad to have me back! Yes, I surely feel that children need Mothers, even though, like me, they can give only moral support. And I make an awfully good boss! . . . Right now we are devoting all our thoughts and energies toward next May when we will have this long-awaited baby. We had given up all hope and had given away all clothes, etc. So now [we] will start all over again collecting.*

*Our Christmas will be a very happy one this year because we'll be all together.*

I was ten years old at the time. With Mom at home, there was a renewed anticipation in the air. My fondest dream was to find an electric train under the tree on Christmas morning. Since I had never owned such a train, that was all I could think about—in particular, a certain kind of Lionel train I had admired in a local store. It included a locomotive that whistled a soothing tone and displayed four big drive wheels on each side, plus a variety of cars, including a crane car and caboose. When Mom arrived from California, she had several packages with her that I was told not to open. Could it be that one of them contained that wonderful train? Each night leading to Christmas, I would lie in bed dreaming about such a gift.

Imagine our eagerness on Christmas morning when it was time to open the packages so beautifully adorned with colored gift wrap and ribbons. When it was my turn, I was shocked by the discovery. There was not *one* train but *two* wrapped just for me! It seemed that both Dad and Mom, separated by such a long distance, had each bought me a train, not knowing the other was doing the same!

Because of the surprise, they gave me an important choice—which Lionel train would I keep? It was not a difficult decision to make, since the train Dad had bought was exactly the one I had been longing for in the toy store, where it had gone around and around the track in an endless rhythm. Mom's train was wonderful too, so I felt a little uncomfortable with my decision, but Mom, as always, came up with a solution to make everyone happy. We would give the extra train to a needy family!

Now we had a problem. Who would get the train? I remember discussing it as a family, talking about finding another home where such a valuable gift was not likely to show up on Christmas. We decided that we would give the train to a family that had emigrated from Denmark to our small town a few years previous. The father was serving as the caretaker of our public school at the time, and to earn extra money, he also delivered milk to the homes in our town with his horse-drawn wagon, charging ten cents a quart—a bargain to be sure. He and his wife were wonderful people, with three sons and a daughter. It was apparent that the family did not have money to spare.

So on Christmas Day, we delivered the beautiful second train to this family. And how surprised and delighted they were to receive such an amazing gift—especially the boys, all of them somewhat older than I. The parents were overjoyed too.

Later that day, I remember hearing a knock on our door. They had all come to pay us a visit. The mother had baked dozens and dozens of delicious Danish cookies for us and had packed them in what seemed to me a huge box. Each cookie was frosted with care using the most enticing and delectable icing in a blend of red-and-green Christmas colors. We feasted on those cookies for weeks. Not one cookie went to waste (although perhaps some went a little bit to waist). It was like having another warm Chinook wind blow through our home. When I played with my own Lionel train, I could often imagine the neighbor boys enjoying the extra train in their own home. It made me feel glad inside.

Not long after that Christmas, my mother gave birth to our little brother, Robert. But in giving birth, my mother lost her life. It was a devastating loss. But I will never forget the lessons she taught me, the love she gave me, and the happiness she brought me.

The Lionel train has gone the way of all mortal objects. The Chinook winds are now but a reminiscence. But the precious memories and abiding gratitude remain living realities as I look forward to the time, one day, when in the coming world I will once again embrace my mom and express to her my heartfelt thanks for the eternal gifts she has given to me and to all of her loved ones.

That will be an eternal Christmas.

# An Unexpected Rescue

BY JENNY PROCTOR

If I tilted my head all the way back, resting it on the seat, I could see the stars through the van's rear window. I stayed that way, with my neck arched and my eyes cast upward, until my muscles ached, begging me to shift my position and stretch my shoulders. But I wouldn't even do it then. If I looked away, I might miss Santa. And I knew he was up there somewhere.

After all, it was after midnight. Technically, I guess, that made it Christmas, but it still felt like Christmas Eve to my family. We'd been in the car an hour already and had three more to drive before we were home. Weird, I know, driving at midnight on Christmas Eve. But it was our family's tradition. Every Christmas Eve afternoon, we piled into the car and drove the four hours to Grandma's house, where food and cousins were plentiful, and we would eat and exchange presents, then pick up our little bags of ribbon candy, chocolate, and walnuts Grandma made for us before leaving again. With thirteen of her own children, Grandma had more grandkids and great-grandkids than I ever even tried to count. There were so many of us that little bags of candy were all she could manage. But we didn't mind.

"I don't think I'm going to see him," I said to my sister. I guess she thought she was too old to stare out the window. I don't remember her glancing at the stars even *once*.

"You might," she said. "Just keep watching."

And so I watched the twinkling stars, looking for something, anything that might be a sign of Santa Claus streaking across the December sky. I broke off a piece of orange ribbon candy and popped it into my mouth, wondering if Santa would get to our house before we'd made it home. It might be kind of fun to walk in the front door and see the presents already there. Mom said she thought he'd wait for us, but I wasn't so sure. How would he even know we weren't home? Seems like that would be a lot to keep up with—what kids were traveling and when.

"How much longer?" my brother asked after a while from the middle seat.

"Just two hours now," Dad called.

Two more hours? Why did time have to move so slowly on Christmas Eve?

"Just listen to the music, guys," Mom said. "Listen to the words and remember why we celebrate Christmas. I'm sure Mary felt very impatient while waiting for the Christ child to be born. I bet she didn't complain, and I bet she wasn't near as comfortable on the back of a donkey as you are in this van." Mom turned up the music, Michael McLean's *The Forgotten Carols* drowning out the impatient whines coming from the back of the van.

When the van lurched and sputtered, I sat up, finally rubbing the ache out of my shoulders.

"What happened?" my sister asked.

The van was still moving but only just. My dad turned off the music and leaned forward, listening to the rattling and groaning of the van's engine. Something was terribly wrong.

We limped up an exit ramp and into a gas station parking lot, where my dad, with a long face and worried eyes, went inside to see if there was anyone who could take a look at our car. The gas station attendant followed my dad back out to the car, and Dad popped the hood. Through his open door, I could hear their conversation.

"I'm not a mechanic," the attendant said. "But my brother is. I could probably get him to take a look at it tomorrow."

"Nothing before then?" my dad asked. "It's Christmas. We'd like to get home tonight if that's possible."

"I guess I can see if he'll drive over and take a look. Give me a minute." He walked back into the gas station and picked up the phone, probably not realizing there were six sets of eyes watching him, hoping he would come back with good news.

Finally, he hung up the phone and walked to the door. "He'll be here in ten minutes," he called.

I could almost feel the big sigh of relief that came from my dad.

A very sleepy mechanic showed up a few minutes later. Dad shook his hand and thanked him for coming, and we all waited to see what he would say about the car.

It wasn't good news.

"You need a new belt," he said. "I can get you one, but it'll take a couple days to get here. I'm sorry I can't help before then."

My heart sank as I realized what the man's words meant for us. We were spending Christmas Eve night sleeping in our van, at a gas station, two hours from home.

"Is there a hotel close by?" I heard my mom ask. "Is there somewhere we could stay?"

A hotel was a little better, but it still wasn't home. And on Christmas morning? All I wanted was to be at *home*.

At first I didn't think much of the long silver Cadillac that had pulled into the gas station parking lot. But when the driver approached my dad, it was hard *not* to notice him. He wore a shiny silver tracksuit, matching pants and jacket, and had a long, full beard. He looked . . . jovial, friendly, and seemed concerned about my family. To me, it didn't make any sense. Did happy guys in silver tracksuits and fancy cars generally go looking for distressed families in the middle of the night on Christmas Eve?

"I'm Roger," the man said. "What seems to be the problem?"

After agreeing there was nothing to be done for the car before the following day, Roger offered to drive my family to the nearest hotel, a couple of exits up the highway.

"It's Christmas Eve," Roger said. "It's the very least I can do."

It was nice of him, sure. But we all were disappointed anyway. No belgian waffles, no stockings on Christmas morning, no Christmas music or presents under the tree. Just a lonely, drab hotel room to celebrate Christmas.

"It can't be helped, kids," my mother whispered. "We'll do the best we can and get home tomorrow. It will be just fine."

Roger's wife, Teddy, climbed out of the Cadillac and helped us all in. It wasn't exactly the easiest fit, squeezing six extra people into a Cadillac, but we managed. Teddy slid across the broad bench seat and sat right next to Roger so my dad and little brother could sit in the front, and the rest of us piled into the backseat. When we were all wedged in, Roger took off down the highway.

He asked us where we were from and if we were excited about the holidays. We did our best to answer politely. Roger and Teddy seemed very kind, and I was glad to not be sitting in the gas station parking lot, but it was hard not to feel like the spirit of Christmas had been sucked right out of the entire night. If we weren't there to sleep in our beds, I wondered, would Santa even come at all?

Through the front window of the Cadillac, I saw a Holiday Inn sign up ahead. That was probably where Roger was taking us—the Holiday Inn—except I doubted it was going to feel much like a holiday.

When the exit ramp leading to the hotel came and went, I saw my parents exchange worried glances. My heart started to race. Why were they worried? And where were Roger and his fancy Cadillac taking us?

His wife must have wondered the same thing. She leaned over.

"Roger," she whispered. "You just passed the hotel. *Where* are you going?"

"It's Christmas Eve, Teddy," Roger said. "And there are children in this car. They don't need to be in a hotel room on Christmas morning; they need to be in their own house, in their own beds."

The night was more than half gone when Roger dropped us off at our front door, which meant it was probably close to Christmas morning when, after their two-hour return trip, he and Teddy finally made it back home. I'm guessing it wasn't exactly how they had expected to spend their Christmas Eve, but Roger acted like it was the simplest thing in the world.

My parents thanked him over and over again.

"Don't even worry about it," he said. "It's Christmas. These children deserve to have the Christmas they were expecting."

Santa hadn't come yet when we arrived home, and Mom hurried us to bed, telling us we'd better get to sleep quickly so Santa would have plenty of time to drop off our presents. But after our unexpected ride home, thinking about Santa Claus and his sleigh full of presents didn't seem all that important.

The true Christmas spirit wasn't in Santa's sleigh streaking across the dark night sky. It wasn't in piles of presents, stuffed stockings, or even plates full of belgian waffles. For my family on that Christmas Eve so many years ago, the true spirit of Christmas was inside a fancy Cadillac and in the kind face and warm generosity of a man in a silver tracksuit.

It's funny though—in my mind's eye, if I trade the silver tracksuit for crushed red velvet and swap the sleek Cadillac for a team of reindeer, Roger, with his long beard and twinkling eyes, looks *just like* Santa Claus.

OTHER BOOKS AND AUDIO BOOKS
BY JENNY PROCTOR

*The House at Rose Creek*

*Mountains Between Us*

# Ned Winder's Christmas

BY MIKE WINDER, GRANDSON AND NEIGHBOR

My children are the sixth generation of Winders to live on Winder Lane, the tree-lined private road leading up to Winder Farms in West Valley City, Utah. My parents live two doors down, closest to the dairy. Grandpa and Grandma Winder's home is next door, and cousins and aunts and uncles live in the other homes. Winder Lane consists of occasional speed bumps, seven homes, and the dairy campus of the Winder Country Store, milk processing plant, and Winder Farms offices.

The houses are all on the east side of the lane, with Valley View Memorial Park—a cemetery founded by family members back in the fifties on some excess farmland—on the west side. Tall trees filled with bird nests, thick bushes where ducks hide, and a cheerful little stream serve as a buffer between the lane and the cemetery. The dead make great neighbors. They don't bark or have loud parties, but their visitors do cause quite the traffic on Memorial Day! In its heyday, the family ran the cemetery, the dairy, and a bakery that was part of the dairy. Grandpa Ned used to joke that the Winder business slogan should be "Drink our milk, eat our bread, and let us bury you when you're dead!"

Oh, Grandpa Ned! His colorful personality was legendary in his day. He had a way of brightening up everyone he met and always leaving smiles in his wake. There is a void in the world since he passed away in the summer of 2005. That August, he moved from his home on the east side of Winder Lane to rest in peace in his cemetery plot on the west side.

Winder Lane is beautiful in all seasons but especially in the winter. As I look out my front window on the lane covered in white, the snow continues to fall. Its hypnotic peacefulness causes me to think of years gone by. There is no more magical season than Christmas. And on Winder Lane, there was no more magical presence than Ned Winder.

\* \* \*

Ned woke up early that December day. Of course, as a former milkman, he habitually woke early. He quietly got ready for work, taking care not to awaken his sweetheart, Gwen. For as much as Ned liked to wake up early, Gwen liked to sleep in. He once quipped that on the morning of the First Resurrection, he'd have to come back later in the day for his Gwennie.

He carefully put a red sock on one foot and a green one on the other. Usually, he matched his socks, but this was the Christmas season, and having one red sock and one green was yet another way to celebrate the time of year and put a smile on someone's face.

He slicked his dark hair with Brylcreem, as usual, and opened his bathroom cabinet to choose a toothbrush. There before him were seventeen toothbrushes hanging upside down in a neat row, each on its respective little nail. Nothing bothered Ned worse than a soggy toothbrush, so he reached out and grabbed the one used least recently in his rotation and enjoyed the firm bristles.

As Ned left the house, he looked around his yard with some sense of satisfaction. The sun was just coming up, but he could still see the Christmas lights that enveloped the bushes. He gazed up at the streamers of Christmas bulbs descending from the trees on the lane, and he smiled wide as he looked back at his brick home. Decades before *National Lampoon's Christmas Vacation* made its debut, Ned Winder was Utah's Clark Griswold. Over seventeen thousand lights adorned the 1950s rambler, and Ned was excited to turn them on later that evening after finishing his magnum opus—a peach tree on the north side of the house that held as many lights as any Christmas masterpiece on Temple Square.

But there was no time to fuss with the lights this morning. Ned put on his coat, pulled on his Jersey gloves, and bounded up the lane toward the dairy. The previous night's snow had created a virtual white tunnel through the large trees, and Ned thought there was not a more beautiful street in the Salt Lake Valley.

Soon he came to the Money Tree. Near the top of the lane, a special tree branched off in two directions just a few feet above the ground. Each of the sides had grown tall like the other trees on the lane, but the split had created a special pocket where Ned loved to toss his spare change. Generations of Winder kids would check the Money Tree when they were in the area, often delighting to find a few coins. Ned smiled to himself, wondering which child would find a little Christmas magic in the Money Tree later that day.

In the dairy yard, he greeted each employee with a warm handshake. As he did each Christmas season, he reached into his pocket and gave each employee he met a crisp five-dollar bill. It wasn't much, but it was an extra surprise on any given December day. A funny saying here and a little joke there, Ned scattered sunshine as he traversed the dairy yard that morning, greeting everyone he came across. He gathered a few quarts of eggnog from the large walk-in icebox adjacent to the milk plant and a box of sweet rolls from the bakery, then headed back home.

It was time to go to work already, and Ned quickly backed out of his driveway. People often know of Ned Winder's role as a partner in Winder Dairy, but few realize that for thirty years he was also executive secretary to the Missionary Department of the Church.

He was a humble man whose home was not elaborate and who never owned a boat, a motor home, or an RV. But where he did indulge was his car. His maroon Porsche 911 Carrera was known all over town, and with its eponymous "Ned" plates, it could not be missed.

On this winter morning, the Porsche cruised into downtown and dipped into the underground parking garage of the Church Office Building.

"Good morning, Mr. Winder!" the parking attendant shouted as Ned pulled past the booth.

"Merry Christmas, Paul!" Ned replied as he handed the attendant a package of sweet rolls through the window of the Porsche.

Ned found a parking space and got out of the sports car. He pulled a plush cloth out of the trunk and carefully wiped away the moisture that had accumulated from the wet December roads.

Elder David B. Haight walked by and complimented him on how clean his car looked. "You take such good, loving care of that car, don't you?" he said.

Ned smiled. "I love this car. Do you think I could have it sealed to me?"

Elder Haight looked at him with a wry smile, wagged his finger, and said, "Go to your room!"

Once inside the Church Office Building, Ned enjoyed passing around the quarts of eggnog and sweet rolls to all the employees. Though he worked with numerous General Authorities, he always treated the secretaries and other staff members as equally important.

"Merry Christmas," he said to each as he shared the treats and often a kiss on the cheek of the sisters in his friendly, sweet way.

The morning found Ned stuck in an especially long meeting with the Church's Missionary Committee. Apostle Spencer W. Kimball was chairman of the missionary committee at the time, and the meeting was being held in his office.

At one point that morning, Ned was using the little washroom adjoining the office. Having skipped breakfast in his rush, he was pleasantly surprised to find a cellophane package half full of macaroons Elder Kimball had left there.

Ned's favorite cookies were macaroons, and his growling tummy convinced him it'd be fine to sneak just one. But when he bit into the cookie, he found it was as hard as cement and nearly broke a tooth! Embarrassed to put a cookie with his teeth marks in it back, he pocketed it and returned to the meeting.

As the conversation wound down, Elder Kimball asked the group if anyone else had anything to add. Elder Bruce R. McConkie said no. Elder Thomas S. Monson said no. And Elder Theodore Tuttle said no. But the committee's secretary raised his hand and was called on. "Yes, Ned?"

Ned pulled the teeth-marked cookie out of his pocket and said, "Elder Kimball, I think those macaroons on the back of your toilet are getting really stale, and I just might sue you for busting my teeth!"

The office erupted into laughter, and Elder Kimball laughed especially hard. He thought that was the funniest thing and said, "See, Ned, crime doesn't pay!"

As the employees left the Church Office Building that evening and were gathering their coats, Ned paused to help a few of his female coworkers put their coats on. "You don't have to help me just because I'm a lady," one said.

"I'm helping you because I'm a gentleman," he replied.

The workers, all bundled up to face the cold, descended in crowded elevators to the parking garage.

But before Ned returned to his car, he made a quick stop next door at Temple Square to pick up a few strands of lights that his friend Helmut had repaired for him. Being friends with the head of Temple Square's light display came in handy this time of year! He had saved his last quart of eggnog for Helmut and thanked him for his help with the lights.

"Thank you, Ned," Helmut said in his thick German accent. "And good luck with the lights!"

As Ned cruised back to Winder Lane after his day at the Church Office Building, he thought about how much he enjoyed working with the Brethren. They had grown to love him and appreciate his sense of humor. *What better work to be engaged in at Christmastime*, he thought, *than in helping Christ continue to build His kingdom on the earth.*

After supper, Ned went out to put the finishing touches on his masterpiece tree. At the time, Ned's home boasted the largest light display on any private residence in the state. In the years to come, the newspapers were sure to include his home on their list of must-see holiday displays.

As he stood on the ladder and reached out to put on yet another strand of lights, a fuse blew, and every light went out. He lumbered down the ladder and went inside to see what had tripped the breakers. Sheepishly, Gwen confessed that when she'd opened the icebox door, it had blown out all the lights! They shared a good laugh, but Ned warned the family to be careful so they didn't run too many appliances while the lights were on.

Having reset the breaker, Ned headed out to finish decorating the peach tree. It was getting dark. This, of course, made the seventeen thousand lights even more spectacular, and Ned smiled despite his cold nose. He was adding the final touches to each carefully wrapped branch when a car pulled into the driveway from the lane. *Oh, how nice*, Ned thought. *Someone is taking the time to pull in to compliment me on my lights.*

The window was rolled down, and the lady in the car looked up at Ned on his stepladder. "Hey, mister," she bellowed. "Can't you widen this road of yours?" Ned was uncharacteristically speechless as the car pulled back out of the driveway and continued down narrow Winder Lane.

*Does anyone appreciate all these lights?* he thought to himself. *Are the hours and hours of putting these up worth it?* He was too much of an optimist to let one crank get him down, but as he lay in bed that night, he said a silent prayer. "Father, may these beautiful Christmas lights bring some joy, some light of Christ into someone's soul this season."

Ned awoke a little earlier than normal the next day and was unsure why. But once his mind was awhirl, he realized it was still dark and he could flip on his Christmas lights for the milkmen to enjoy as they headed down from the dairy to make their deliveries.

Ned breathed a sigh of relief as the breakers held. And why shouldn't they, since few appliances were running when everyone else was asleep? He walked into the lane to admire his handiwork.

While standing in the road, looking at his twinkling home, he heard sounds coming from the cemetery behind him. He walked into the cemetery and saw a woman mourning near a fresh grave. Ned did not want to intrude, so he watched her from behind the trees for a moment before returning home. How sad she seemed! he thought, and his kind heart ached.

As he walked up his driveway, Ned heard the woman get into her car. He noticed she was now driving out of the cemetery and up the lane. He watched as she slowly drove by the spectacle of lights and then went on to turn around at the top of the lane by the dairy. Ned quickly went into the house and grabbed an extra package of sweet rolls, and then he stood out in the lane.

He hailed her to stop as she drove back down, and when she did, she rolled down the car window.

"Good morning!" Ned said cheerfully. "You're the first person to visit my lights today, and you won a package of fresh Winder Dairy sweet rolls!"

The shocked woman reached out and accepted the pastries. She became very emotional and, through the tears, muttered a perfunctory "Thank you."

Ned smiled warmly at her and replied, "Isn't it great to think of the Savior this time of year?"

The puzzled woman asked, "Why are you doing this?"

"Because you're my sister, and I love you," Ned replied to the stranger.

Feeling concerned, he watched the car roll over the speed bumps and down the lane, and then he headed back inside for breakfast.

As Ned was eating his breakfast, the phone rang. It was the woman calling to thank him for brightening her morning.

"My husband passed away recently, and I was visiting his grave. I'm alone now and so depressed," she explained. "While I was at the cemetery, I was thinking I might go home and take my own life." Then she said, "Your visit with me on the lane cheered me up and gave me hope. There is good in the world, none of us are alone, and we do indeed have a Savior. Thank you, thank you," she cried, bringing tears to Ned's eyes. "You saved my life today!"

*This Christmas tale is a compilation of true stories that took place over a number of holiday seasons. The author appreciates your indulgence, as they are grouped together for literary effect.*

# The Best Christmas Ever

BY M. R. DURBIN

*Lowell is my father. I write this story in honor of him. He passed away on June 25, 2014, as I was in the process of working on this story for publication. This memory will be a special Christmas present for our family.*

Twelve-year-old Lowell awoke to the clunk of wood being stuffed into the iron cookstove in the kitchen. The early-morning rhythm of shuffling feet, the muted voices of his parents, Wallace and Mar, and the dim light from the single bulb hanging from the ceiling in the kitchen all presaged the expected darkening of the door as Lowell's father stuck his head in and softly called, "Come on, boys. We've got chores to do before we can leave."

Leave! Suddenly, Lowell remembered. Today they would be traveling up Dry Fork Canyon to cut down a Christmas tree. Throwing back the quilt, he swung his legs out onto the cold board floor, helped by a shove in the back by his older brother, fourteen-year-old Larry.

"Knock it off!" Lowell growled as he pulled the quilt off the bed in retaliation to Larry's antics and snort of laughter. Like most brothers, they shared a complex relationship of equal doses of companionship and sibling rivalry.

Quickly, the two pulled on their pants and flannel shirts, then knelt to lace up their leather boots, stiff from the cold. Lowell finished first, stood, and gave Larry a soft push on the shoulder, sending him tumbling over onto his side before escaping into the kitchen.

They lived in a small house on a ranch Uncle Hugh Colton owned. Uncle Hugh was the grandson of Philander Colton of Mormon Battalion fame and was actually Lowell's mother's uncle. But only six years separated them in age, and all the children knew Hugh as Uncle Hugh.

While attending law school in Washington, D.C., Uncle Hugh and his friend Willard Marriott had started a small root beer stand to help pay their way through school. When Marriott wanted to continue to expand the business, Uncle Hugh sold his share to Marriott for $5,000, choosing to return to the Uintah Basin to practice law. Since Uncle Hugh was now a successful lawyer in Vernal and owned one of the largest ranches in the Ashley Valley area, it was obvious he had made a wise decision. Now, as Christmas 1944 approached, Uncle Hugh was serving as a colonel in the 1104th Combat Engineer Corps with General Eisenhower, building strategic bridges over the Ruhr River. While Hugh was gone, Wallace was being paid thirty dollars each month to run his ranch.

Lowell crossed through his parents' bedroom, noticing the lump that was his younger sister, Eloise, still curled up under the quilt in the corner, and made his way into the dimly lit room that served as a combination kitchen, living room, and dining room. He stood near the now-warming stove as he struggled into his heavy coat and hat.

How spacious the house seemed to be since Wallace had found a small, old log cabin on the ranch and had used the large draft horses to drag it to the house and attach it as a bedroom for the two boys.

Then Lowell's older sisters, Betty, nineteen, and Barta, seventeen, moved to Downey, California, to be with the Roy Carrol family, who had been instrumental in getting Wallace and Mar and the children sealed in the Salt Lake Temple a mere five years previously. The Carrols had moved to California at the start of the war and had invited the two girls to live with them and work in the Consolidated-Vultee Aircraft plant building trainer aircraft. Lowell, who had been out of the Uintah Basin only once in his life—and that was a three-day trip to Salt Lake—often tried to imagine what that would be like. The girls had taken the bus, a two-day trip to a city by the ocean. What an adventure a trip like that would be. Some people had all the luck.

As Lowell and Larry finished getting ready, they cast curious glances toward the two boxes stacked in the corner of the room. The mysterious boxes had arrived in the post two days previously, surprise Christmas gifts from Betty and Barta. The two boys had been expecting the usual Christmas gifts, an orange in their stocking and maybe a small toy, often carved by one of the hands on the ranch. Gifts of this size from such a far-off place were almost unimaginable.

"What do you think they are?" Lowell whispered, staring at the two boxes.

Larry shrugged, trying to appear uninterested, as was the duty of older brothers, but he failed miserably. "Don't know. Probably underwear or something."

"Naw." Lowell shook his head. "I already got a pair, and they don't even have any holes in 'em yet. And those boxes are way too big for just underwear."

"You boys, get those cows milked," Wallace said, interrupting their speculation and chasing them out the door.

"This is going to be the best Christmas ever," Lowell whispered to Larry as they stepped out into the crisp, dark morning.

The boys' breath puffed in short clouds as they trudged toward the barn, their boots crunching in the dry snow. They had five cows to milk and feed and seventeen chickens to feed and gather eggs from. Much of the milk would be sold to the local dairy, while many of the eggs would be sold to neighbors for much-needed extra cash.

The barn smelled of dry hay, warm manure, dusty grain, old potatoes, and musky, warm animals. The steady thrum-thrum of the milk as it squirted into the buckets filled the silence as each boy balanced on milk stools, concentrating on hitting the middle of the bucket and preventing the cow from kicking it over.

"Maybe they're new boots," Lowell mumbled, partly to himself.

A spray of milk hit him behind the ear.

"Hey!" he complained as he momentarily stopped his milking and reached up to wipe away the moisture. "Knock it off."

"It's not boots." Larry didn't need to be told that Lowell was referring to the mysterious boxes. "Those boxes aren't quite big enough for boots. Besides, where would they get boots in California? I hear it's so warm there everybody goes barefoot all the time."

Morning chores were followed by a breakfast of eggs, toast, oatmeal, and milk strained and chilled from the night before. As was their custom, before eating, each member of the family knelt by their chair, and Wallace offered the morning prayer and blessing on the food.

Scarcely stopping to breathe, the boys wolfed down breakfast, their minds split between the adventure of the day and the mysterious boxes stacked in the corner. Although there were also presents for Eloise, Mar, and Wallace, it was the two mysterious twin boxes that riveted their attention.

Larry reached across the table, his eyes on the boxes across the room. "Pass the butter," he demanded.

Lowell, noticing the lack of attention, picked up the butter dish and extended it toward Larry's outstretched hand, giving it one last thrust that buried Larry's thumb deep into the mound of butter.

"Hey!" Larry exclaimed, turning in anger just in time to see Lowell's mischievous grin, but further remonstrations were quickly squelched by a sharp look from both parents.

Following breakfast, the boys harnessed two small horses to the wagon, which was just like any other farm wagon: a box on two axles, reminiscent of the old pioneer wagons, except this one had been modernized with metal spoke wheels and rubber tires. The two horses, although small, were strong and could pull the wagon for hours at a trot without tiring.

As the early-morning sun rose over the eastern hills and the fog lifted among the cottonwoods along Ashley Creek, the family started north. Wallace and Mar sat on the seat, Wallace holding the reins, and the two boys and Eloise huddled under quilts in the back of the wagon. The journey up Dry Fork to Grandma's house was fifteen miles and would take several hours.

Grandma Caldwell lived in a house with two large rooms and a loft. The house sat on the ground originally homesteaded by her grandfather, Matthew Caldwell. Matthew had been a citizen of Hancock County, Illinois, when the Mormons had first come, had married a Mormon girl, and had known many of the early Church leaders. Accepting the challenge by Brigham Young to be baptized at Mt. Pisgah, he had joined the Church and then Mormon Battalion only a few days later and had eventually settled here in Dry Fork Canyon.

Grandma's house was always a welcome diversion for the whole family. Set in the middle of the flat floor of the canyon bisected by Ashley Creek, the farmland stretched for about a quarter of a mile between steep walls of yellow sandstone and juniper-covered hills. Not only was it a haven from the mundane chores that seemed to govern their life on the ranch, but it also offered access to one very special modern-day miracle—Grandma had a radio. Here they could listen to news of the war firsthand. Here, through the magic of the airwaves, they followed the exploits of their Uncle Ked, a soldier in "The Big Red One," as he fought his way across North Africa, Sicily, and up through Italy.

But as heroic as Uncle Ked was, there was one thing on the radio that was even more important. The biggest sporting event in the world was boxing, and the greatest boxer in the world was Joe Louis. Every Friday night they could get to Grandma's, they listened intently to the latest war news and then the most important event, the Friday-night fight, and if they were really lucky, it was Joe Louis's fight.

\* \* \*

Friday, December 22, dawned bright and clear. Once again loaded in the wagon, the family traveled another five miles up Dry Fork until they left the junipers behind and the mountainside gave way to white pine and blue spruce.

Larry waded through the knee-deep snow, carefully inspecting each tree, looking for the perfect Christmas tree, when he felt a sharp sting behind his left ear. Quickly, his hand raised to the spot, and he turned back. "Hey, knock it off!"

"Knock what off?" Lowell asked innocently, even as he threw another juniper berry, this time hitting Larry in the forehead.

"You know what," Larry responded, half angry, half caught up in the horseplay. "Hit me again and I'll give you a good old Joe Louis right cross and knock you into the middle of next week."

"Wishful thinking," Lowell responded as he threw yet another berry at his brother, causing him to duck. Laughing, Lowell dashed away and dodged a snowball Larry threw as he himself laughed at the banter.

Late in the afternoon, the family returned triumphantly, having successfully stalked the wily Christmas tree. They quickly consumed a dinner of hot stew and warm bread before the family settled down for their second evening at Grandma's house and the highly anticipated war news and the Friday-night fight.

Grandma adjusted the radio to rid it of static as they listened intently to reports that earlier in the day, a U.S. air raid composed of over one hundred Superfortress B-29 bombers, led by General Emmett "Rosie" O'Donnel, had completed the first mass air raid over Tokyo. In Europe, the Nazis had begun a major offensive in a place called the Ardennes, and the battle that ensued came to be known as the Battle of the Bulge. The 101st Airborne had been completely surrounded but, so far, had refused to surrender. Cloudy skies prevented American air support, but General Patton was rushing through severe winter conditions to rescue the brave Americans.

The boys were disappointed to hear the fight that night was not Joe Louis's. They had last heard Joe Louis fight Dan Merritt in an exhibition fight in Chicago back on November 24. The fight had lasted only three rounds, and Louis had won easily.

Tonight the fight was between two middleweights, Rocky Graziano and Harold Green, at Madison Square Garden, and New York City mayor Fiorello H. LaGuardia was in attendance. The fight was a good one in which each fighter knocked the other down, and Green won in a decision in ten rounds.

"Joe Louis could'a beat either one of 'em," Larry declared as he prepared for bed in the loft.

"Joe Lois could'a beat both of 'em at the same time," Lowell affirmed as he blew out the candle.

* * *

When they returned to the ranch Saturday afternoon, the house was cold and the boxes were still waiting for them. They started a fire in the kitchen stove, and the boys wasted no time in helping their father put up the tree in the corner of the room. Carefully, Mar pulled a box containing a long string of colored lightbulbs from a closet, and before long the tree was transformed into a magical display of colored electric lights reflected by long strands of silver tinsel.

Not long after those mystical boxes were placed beneath the tree's branches, the two boys reluctantly took buckets outside, filled them with ice-cold water, and lugged them back into the house, where they were placed on the stove to warm.

Wallace retrieved the large tin number-three tub from the side of the house and placed it in the middle of the kitchen floor. The next day was the Sabbath, and Saturday night was bath night. Mar insisted the entire family bathe every Saturday night, whether they needed it or not.

* * *

Sunday, Christmas Eve, dawned bright and cold. Hoar frost glistened thick on the Russian Olives that grew along the canal, and the family had to squint against the morning sunlight reflecting off the snow as they walked the quarter of a mile to church. Christmas hymns, talks of Mary and donkeys and Wise Men and babes in mangers filled the hours, and through it all, neither Lowell nor Larry could take their minds off the two mysterious boxes waiting under the tree.

* * *

In the darkness of that early Christmas morning, Wallace stuck his head through the door and softly called, "Come on, boys. We've got chores to—"

Wallace was startled to see his two young sons not under the covers as usual but standing in the middle of the room, their anxious faces belying the fact that chores were not the first things on their minds.

"Hmm," he mused, struggling to keep his smile from showing. "Looks like you're more anxious than those cows."

"Aw. C'mon, Dad," Larry pleaded. "Can't we open those presents from Betty and Barta first?"

Wallace tried to look stern, though his face was largely hidden in shadow. "Those cows still need milked."

Lowell nodded his head, eager to please. "We'll do it. But those presents, they'll only take a minute."

Wallace seemed to think it over, then called over his shoulder. "What do you think, Mother? Can we delay those chores?"

"Better to rush through the presents than rush through the milking," she answered from near the stove, giving the two boys hope.

Wallace turned, opening a path through the doorway. "I suppose, but don't be taking too long."

With a shout, the two boys fought to be the first one through the door and past their father. Rushing to the tree, they each grabbed the present with their name on it and began tearing off the brown-paper wrapping. At almost the same instant, the boys had their boxes opened and were staring into the depths with equal measures of delight and wonder. With what almost amounted to reverence, Larry was the first to reach in and pull out his prize, holding it up for all to see.

"Boxing gloves." He breathed almost reverently. "Real, live boxing gloves."

"Just like Joe Louis," Lowell whispered in wonder.

Larry struggled to force his hand into one of his new gloves. "I'm going to knock your head off." He grunted with a grin as he struggled to loosen the strings on the wrist.

"You'll have a hard time doing that while you're lying on your back," Lowell returned, excitement in his own voice.

"That's the Christmas spirit," Mar mumbled from across the kitchen.

Wallace's shadow moved between the boys. "Neither one of you is going to do anything until those chores are done."

Reluctantly, both boys gently replaced their new boxing gloves under the tree, then, like taking medicine, rushed to don their clothes and complete their morning chores.

"Pow, pow." Lowell threw shadow punches as he pulled on his coat.

"You're going to beg for mercy," Larry warned him, his wide smile engulfing his face.

"I'm going to be begging you to get back up off the floor," Lowell said.

Soon the sound of the door banging shut as the boys rushed out toward the barn accentuated the last words Lowell spoke as he left the warmth of the house. "This is going to be the best Christmas ever."

* * *

Mar stood by the window, watching her two boys rush toward the barn.

"What were those two girls thinking, sending those boys boxing gloves?" She slowly shook her head. "They know they'll just spend the day hurting and bruising each other."

Wallace put his arm across his wife's shoulders. "I suppose they were thinking just like big sisters: imagining their little brothers hurting and bruising each other and thinking, that might just make this the best Christmas ever!"

OTHER BOOKS AND AUDIO BOOKS
BY M. R. DURBIN

*Swords of Joseph*

# The Tommy Tree

BY KRISTEN MCKENDRY

*As shared by my friend Rita van der Heiden. Names used with permission.*

Nineteen ninety-four was a year of transition.

My lovely sister Mary Ann blended her family with Bruce's, joining her two children with his three and making plans to move into a new home big enough for all of them around Christmastime. It would be a wonderful, exciting new beginning—a new family, a new home, and a new life together.

Mary Ann's son Tommy was a fun, handsome kid, a practical joker with a wry sense of humor. He had dark hair and an engaging smile and, at fourteen, was the youngest of the five children. Fourteen was his favorite number, and he even wore fourteen on his hockey jersey. But ironically, on September 14, 1994, just two weeks after he started high school, all that energy and promise was lost.

Tommy was riding his bike with a friend when he attempted to cross a street near his home. A newly licensed teenager driving his car at twice the legal speed struck Tommy, and Tommy went through the windshield. His friend raced to get my sister, and as soon as Mary Ann arrived, she knelt on the road, holding her son in her arms. He was breathing but unconscious. When the paramedics arrived, they transported him to the local hospital but then immediately took him to the regional medical center. Doctors found he had no brain activity, and after much anguish, the family decided to remove him from life support the next day.

Suddenly, everything was in turmoil. The plans, the hope, and the happiness were in shambles. Anger, loss, and a deep internal protest took their place. This was not what was supposed to happen. Not to Tommy, not now, not in this way. I watched the pain engulf my beautiful sister.

Somehow, the family got through the next few months, but as Christmas approached, no one knew what to do. We wanted to make it a happy holiday for the other children, but no one knew how to handle it. Some of us had private conversations to try to figure it out. How could we be sensitive to Mary Ann's and Bruce's feelings? How could we gather for our traditional celebration with such a gaping hole in our hearts? How could we make right something that was entirely wrong? And who was going to make the first move to face what no one wanted to face?

On top of all of this, I was going through transitions of my own. I had just moved back to Canada with my two little girls from living in the U.S., my marriage at a sudden end and my future uncertain. My little girls, Sam and Alex, ages six and four, were just adapting to our new life in Canada without their father, and they had their own additional hurts to be mindful of. I wanted Christmas to be special for them.

All in all, it was a difficult time. I fretted for days, wanting to make some gesture to comfort my sister, wanting to acknowledge Tommy's absence but not wanting to overdo it. What would be too much? What would be too little? Should I do anything at all? What would the rest of the family think if I did do something? Would they be upset or relieved?

Whatever I did, I wanted it to be just the right thing. Christmas, I knew, had to be handled very carefully this year.

Finally, I went outside the family to speak with several friends about my dilemma. I thought maybe their more-removed perspective would help.

"I don't know whether to mention Tommy's name or not," I explained. "No one wants to bring him up, but it has to be managed somehow. You can't get around the fact it's their first Christmas in their new house without the son who should have been there. I don't know what to say."

"It won't matter what you say," a friend told me. "It won't take away what happened. And anyway, it's not about saying the right thing. There is no right thing. You need to just allow *them* to say what *they* need to say. Just be with them, nurture them, and let them know you haven't forgotten him. Keep that door open so they can let him back into the room whenever they need to without making you feel awkward."

This felt right to me. After a lot of pondering and prayer, I thought I knew what to do.

That Christmas the family gathered at Mary Ann and Bruce's home—in-laws, cousins, a house packed with people. When I arrived, I gave Mary Ann a little gift bag. Inside was a Christmas-tree ornament, a hand-blown glass droplet. I had put a tag on it that said, "*To Tommy, Christmas 1994, with love from Tante Rita, Alex, and Sam.*" (Our family is Dutch, and *tante* is Dutch for *aunt*.)

I watched my sister's face closely as she opened the gift. She was still for a moment, and then she turned to me with shining eyes.

"This is perfect," she said, and she went to place the ornament on the tree.

It was still awkward, with everyone not knowing whether to bring up Tommy's name or not, but the first step had been taken. I knew I had done the right thing with my gift when Mary Ann showed me how she had hung Tommy's stocking along with all the others. She had placed a rose in it to honor his presence with us that Christmas.

We gathered for our annual gift giving and tried to carry on as usual. Then, after all the presents had been opened, I pulled out one last gift and gave it to Mary Ann.

We all watched as she unwrapped the box. Inside was a package of balloons, some ribbon, and some note cards and colored pens. Mary Ann looked at me questioningly.

"I want to do something to remember Tommy," I told the group. "I know it's been difficult this year, and none of us has known quite how to handle it all. I don't want to not recognize Tommy, because I feel he's here with us today. I tried to come up with an idea, and here it is: I thought maybe we could write messages to Tommy—say whatever we want to. Then we can tie them to the balloons and release them. You don't have to do this, Mary Ann, but we're here to help you if you decide it's what you want to do." And I pulled out a canister of helium that I'd hidden.

There was a pause, and then someone said something about balloons not being environmentally friendly. That cut the tension, and we began to snicker.

"God is just going to have to forgive us on this one," I replied. "The earth will understand. What do you think, Mary Ann?"

She broke into a broad smile, the haunted look in her eyes finally easing. "Yes," she said.

So we sat around the dining table and wrote messages, the littlest ones drawing pictures on the note cards. We even sipped helium from the balloons to make our voices squeaky, and we laughed and were silly, and we remembered Tommy. An air of excitement ignited the room, a relieving of the anxiety, and it felt like a burden had been lifted from all of us.

We tied the fifteen-or-so balloons together in one big bunch, with our notes tied to the bottoms of the strings. When we were ready, we all trooped outside. It was a beautiful day, the temperature hovering around freezing point. The invigorating air refreshed our lungs. The sky was a clear, crisp blue and showed only a couple of wispy clouds in the distance. We stood together on the front lawn and released the balloons, sending our messages to heaven.

We silently watched them rise higher and higher, all of us caught up in quiet reflection. Some tears were shed, and I know there were some prayers sent heavenward with those messages. Just as the balloons were about to disappear from view, one of the children tugged my elbow.

"Look!"

We all looked, and there was a huge rainbow arching over the clear, cold sky, where no rainbow should have been.

I know it sounds cliché, but it really happened. We all looked at each other in amazement and joy. I turned to Mary Ann and said quietly, "Someone's talking to you."

Months later, when my six-year-old was making valentine cards in class, her school teacher stopped by her desk and complimented her on her drawing.

Little Samantha replied casually, "Thanks. It's for my cousin Tommy. But I'm going to need a balloon."

Every year, I give Mary Ann a new ornament for what the family now calls the Tommy Tree. It's her favorite gift. I watch for the perfect thing as I travel throughout the year and find little ornaments that seem just right for Tommy: homemade things, hand-painted decorations, crocheted angels, pinecone teddy bears, a little figurine of a mouse on hockey skates with a hockey jersey—each is different and has special meaning. This year I am bringing her one I found on a trip to Arizona—a glass ornament hand-painted with purple (Tommy's favorite color) hummingbirds (Mary Ann's favorite). My sister has quietly asked me not to ever stop this tradition.

There will be twenty ornaments on the tree this year. Twenty years without Mary Ann's sweet, funny little boy. Sometimes she wonders if others have forgotten him; time has passed, but his loss is always with her, a hole that will never be filled. But at the same time, Tommy is still a big part of all of our lives. And we have the Tommy Tree to remind us.

A number of years after Tommy died, my sister was considering leaving the big city and moving north to a cottage, but she was torn. How could she leave the cemetery where her son was buried?

A few of us were at the cottage one weekend, helping her clean it, and someone found an old patio stone half buried in the ground. When they pried it up and cleaned it off, they found it was etched with a drawing of an angel. It was such a surprise to find there in the woods. Once again, I looked at Mary Ann and said gently, "Someone's talking to you. He's still with you, no matter where you live." And Mary Ann knew she could make the move.

Tommy has become entwined with Christmas for me now. It seems an especially appropriate time to honor him and others who are gone. It's a time to remember the birth of another boy, born long ago and far away, who also died too young. But that remembrance brings to mind that at Christmastime and whenever we think of Him, we look beyond the dying to the rising and to the life to come.

OTHER BOOKS AND AUDIO BOOKS AUTHORED
OR COAUTHORED BY KRISTEN McKENDRY

*Promise of Spring*

*The Ties That Bind*

*Garden Plot*

*The Worth of a Soul*

*Beyond the White River*

*Desperate Measures*

# Christmas Angel
## BY JEANETTE MILLER

As a child, I loved my younger brothers, David and Michael, but really wished I had a sister. This wasn't the typical hope many girls have when they're young; it was a longing so strong I couldn't explain it. I'd often pester my parents with requests for a new baby sister, but it didn't seem like it would ever happen. Mom didn't feel like she could handle more children, and while David was adopted, her other two deliveries had been brutal.

So, in that secret place in my heart, I imagined a tiny porcelain figurine I had to be the sister I wanted. No more than two inches high, the figure was a sweet little girl kneeling with a blankie, looking cuddly and angelic. I'd take her off the shelf and hold her in my hand, envisioning the love a sister might bring. I knew she would love me and that I would love her back.

When I was nine years old, my mom announced that she was pregnant, and I was ecstatic! She knew how much I wanted a sister and even promised me that this baby would be a girl. In my youthful innocence, I never questioned her. I knew Mom was right! It wasn't until years later that I learned about the recurring dreams Mom had had of a little girl with big brown eyes and soft brown curls. For over five years, these dreams had troubled her, not only because she didn't feel capable of having more children or adopting again but also because we were all blue-eyed blonds. Even my father had had a few dreams of the same little girl, so they assumed the dreams were Heavenly Father's way of letting them know Mom was supposed to have a baby girl.

My parents talked about girl names they liked and prepared for a baby girl to be born. If anyone even suggested it might be a boy, we got a little ruffled because we *knew* it was a girl—my longed-for sister. When Joseph was born, I was devastated. I wept inconsolably. But as soon as he came home from the hospital, I fell in love with him. I mothered him, changed his diapers, and often got up with him at night. I went as far as to hold up a hand to tell my mother "I've got him" when she'd come for him. I adored that baby boy.

It didn't make any sense why Joey wasn't a girl. Mom almost died giving birth to him. But in the hospital, while holding her new baby, Mom saw his little eyes look straight into hers and had a powerful spiritual experience. Joey's adult spirit communicated to her, saying, "Please accept me. I cannot explain to you why I am not who you were expecting, but someday you will understand. Just please love me!" And we did love him, without exception.

Life progressed as usual for our family—we moved around a lot due to my dad's work as an auditor and controller for Del Monte Corporation. We had already lived on a banana plantation in Guatemala and then in Puerto Rico before Joey was born. In 1979, we moved to Costa Rica, where Dad became the financial director for Bandeco (Banana Development Corporation), a subsidiary of Del Monte.

I was thirteen but still had my tiny figurine of the little girl, a tangible reminder of a never-ending wish. Every once in a while, I'd hold her in my hand with tender thoughts before placing her back in my room. In 1982, Mom had a hysterectomy, a final assurance that I'd never have a sister and our family was complete.

After summer vacation and our annual trip to California, I began my junior year of high school. One day when I came home from school, I found my mother crying, and I asked what was wrong. She told me something had happened that she hadn't told anyone about yet. She'd been visiting an orphanage in Santo Domingo de Heredia with some sisters in our ward, our good friends Ella Mae Nájera and Joy Wingo. Joy had adopted a little girl in Utah and was hoping to find a second child to adopt, and Mom had gone along to help out at the orphanage and support her friend.

The orphanage was a small, two-bedroom house with five cribs in each bedroom. As Mom walked inside, she noticed a child still in her crib in the first bedroom. When she turned and looked into the bedroom, goose bumps prickled over her. There, in the crib, sat a one-year-old little girl with big brown eyes and soft brown curls! Mom learned that the little girl's name was María de Los Angeles, which meant "Mary of the Angels." She was called "Marielos" for short.

Mom tried to ignore the stunning resemblance to the little girl in her dreams from years before, but it didn't work. "I just can't stop thinking about her," she cried in confusion.

My immediate response was, "Let's adopt her!"—certainly not what Mom was hoping to hear. But when I suggested that she talk to Dad, she agreed. My dad, a quiet giant, who, in my eyes, could make anything right, simply said, "Well, let's go see her."

The next Saturday, my parents drove to the orphanage in Heredia. When they arrived, something amazing happened. Marielos and a few other children were playing with some of the people who were visiting the orphanage that day. As Dad came inside, Marielos turned and saw him. For a moment, their eyes locked. Then, with arms outstretched, she rushed into his arms with *abrazos y besitos* (hugs and kisses) and didn't let go. It was love at first sight for them. A week later our whole family went to see Marielos, and the same sweet reception occurred. We were all enchanted with her.

I loved babies anyway, but I adored this little girl. She was the life of the orphanage—vivacious, happy, and full of personality. I used to hold one end of a sash with Marielos at the other end, following me around and giggling. When it was time to go, I didn't want to leave her.

As we knelt around my parents' bed for family prayers at night, we often had to count heads because it felt like someone was missing. Mom and Dad . . . me . . . the three boys . . . . We were all there. But it still felt like someone was missing. Could Marielos really be meant for our family? The thought was thrilling, overwhelming, and hard to believe all at the same time! But the more we prayed about it as a family, the surer we felt that this precious little girl was supposed to be ours. She was my sister!

As the holidays approached, we continued visiting the orphanage, expressing our deep interest in Marielos. But we were told she was not up for adoption and that we should forget about her. "*Sería imposible*," they said. "You will only get hurt if your family continues to see her." Foreigners were allowed to adopt only older children or siblings from the orphanages through the Patronato, the government adoption agency in Costa Rica. If Marielos were to be given to anyone, it would be a Costa Rican family. Forget her? *That* was the impossibility! Nothing could keep us from visiting this beautiful olive-skinned child who had captured our hearts. We loved her and believed she was meant to be part of our family.

When I was growing up, my Dad seemed invincible. He could do anything in his quiet strength: he was fluent in Spanish, well respected among his peers, and, at the time, the bishop of our Zapote Ward, *Barrio Uno*. I trusted him completely with the tremendous task of trying to influence the Patronato to reconsider Marielos's case so she could be put up for adoption. Dad's friend, Hernán Robles, the general manager of Bandeco, also began helping us. He knew a woman named Mabel, who was a council member for the Patronato and was on the adoption board. Mabel met with my parents and liked them. She said she would put in a "good word" for us and do all that she could to help us try to adopt Marielos.

One day while Dad was on lunch break, he told us that he had gone to the orphanage to see our little girl. She'd slept in his arms as he'd pled for Heavenly Father's help, promising to do everything in his power to make Marielos ours. He began paperwork with the Patronato, but once again, we were informed that adoption was impossible.

December arrived and, with it, the holiday spirit. Fruit stands popped up on street corners, selling bright red imported apples. Families made preparations for traditional tamales steamed in banana leaves. And the arrival of the dry season brought warmer weather and the lure of sandy beaches for vacations. But that year our minds were focused in another direction, especially with the arrival of wonderful news: Marielos had been declared up for adoption! That Christmas held special meaning to us as we pondered the possibility of bringing home our little girl. It would make it the best Christmas of my life.

We eagerly waited for updates from Mabel about the adoption committee to see when they would review Marielos's case and make a final decision. Although some committee members were opposed to and almost hostile toward us, we knew Heavenly Father heard our prayers, and we trusted Him to bring about a true miracle.

On December 14, Dad got a call from Hernán, who told him the committee had met. By a split decision, they had given Marielos to another family, an older Costa Rican couple with no children. The adoption was final.

There were no words to describe the shock and devastation our family felt. How could this be? It wasn't right! She was mine—my sister! Those people couldn't have her; she belonged with us. I knew that as well as I knew my own heart. How could Heavenly Father let this happen? I wondered. How could He do this?

I was wounded, distraught, and angry with God. Going to church on Sunday, I could barely choke out Christmas carols. My life had been destroyed. How could I sing, how could I go on when everything I'd hoped for had been taken away? I didn't want to celebrate Christmas. But I still had to go through the motions with a cold, heavy heart. The worst thing I had to do was go Christmas caroling at two other orphanages with the Young Women . . . three days before Christmas. How could my heart take such pain, singing "Gloria a Dios" to those beautiful children who reminded me so much of Marielos? As Mom drove me home, we both wept over everything we'd been through. Nothing seemed to make any sense.

When we got home, my dad was quick to greet us at the door. He was acting a little funny. "I have a Christmas present that has to be opened early," he said with a silly grin. "It's in your room, Jeanette." I didn't know what Dad could possibly have bought that needed to be opened before Christmas morning. Shoes? Clothes? Certainly nothing that could compensate for the emptiness I felt. Mom followed me down the terrazzo-floored hallway to my bedroom. I peeked inside. There, in my bed, was a sleeping little angel . . . Marielos! I burst into tears of joy and confusion. What had Dad done? Had he stolen her? I could hardly believe she was there, her curly brown hair poking out of the covers. My baby sister was home . . . but how?

Dad explained that the Costa Rican couple didn't want Marielos after all and had dropped her off at the Patronato offices. They claimed she didn't "adapt." Iris Brenes, the president of the Patronato, who had been so against us from the beginning and had negatively influenced the voting committee, had called my dad at work to say, "If you still want Marielos, she's yours. But come immediately, or she'll be taken back to the orphanage and you'll never see her again."

Dad dropped everything, enlisted the help of his secretary, Indiana, and raced through town to pick up our girl. Señora Brenes reluctantly conceded, "Well, Señor, some things are just meant to be." Then she went into her office and closed the door.

I'd never felt this kind of joy before at Christmastime! Now I knew that Heavenly Father did listen to our prayers and knew all along that there was only one way we could get my sister; even though it didn't happen the way we had planned, it was the way that it needed to be to make her ours.

In Costa Rica, Santa Claus doesn't bring the Christmas presents; the baby Jesus does. And that was exactly how this gift had come. By heavenly miracles, we were given the best Christmas gift of my life . . . the brown-eyed angel who became my sister.

OTHER BOOKS BY JEANETTE MILLER

*Montana Summer*